Of related interest from Faber and Faber

Notes: On the Making of Apocalypse Now by Eleanor Coppola

The Apocalypse Now Book by Peter Cowie

Coppola by Peter Cowie

AN ORIGINAL
SCREENPLAY BY

JOHN
MILIUS

AND

FRANCIS
FORD COPPOLA

faber and faber

First published in the United States in 2001 by
Talk Miramax Books
Hyperion, 77 West 66th Street, New York,
New York 10023-6298

First published in the United Kingdom in 2001
by Faber and Faber Limited
3 Queen Square, London WC1N 3AU

Printed in England by Clays Ltd, St Ives plc

Screenplay prepared by Anahid Nazarian

Photos courtesy of American Zoetrope &
Miramax Films

A CIP record for this book
is available from the British Library

ISBN: 0-571-21484-3

10 9 8 7 6 5 4 3 2 1

INTRODUCTION

by Francis Ford Coppola

I recall first hearing about the idea that was to become the script for *Apocalypse Now* from John Milius and George Lucas, during a time in the late 1960s when I had an office at Warner Brothers and was working as a screenwriter. I had recently been a UCLA film student but was now working professionally, and the fact that I had an office on a studio lot attracted lots of friends from USC and UCLA, including George, John, and Carroll Ballard. Everyone was talking about everything; all the exciting projects they had in their heads. John was telling unbelievable stories about many of his surfer friends who had returned from Vietnam, and the action there. John wanted to write a screenplay about it and alternately called it The *Psychedelic Soldier* or *Apocalypse Now*. These were the early days of the formation of my company, American Zoetrope, and we were all excited about the movies we were going to make. George and John were teaming up to plan *Apocalypse Now* and wanted to shoot it in 16mm somewhere in Stockton; Carroll Ballard was deeply into Conrad's *Heart of Darkness* and was planning to put it in production. I was writing *The Conversation* and wanted to do that. There was a lot of cross-fertilization going on, to say the least, and before I knew it, the description of John's script-to-be included a soldier named Willard going upriver to find a renegade officer named Kurtz. There is no question that Carroll's interest in the Conrad story was in the air and influenced John, although John said he was always planning that structure.

Later that year, I took a big chance (I was the only one actually working). I left my employment at Warner Brothers, sold my house and a small summer house, and used the money to buy sound mixing equipment and a new kind of editing machine from Europe (the Kem and Steenbeck), and our whole group made a mass exodus from Hollywood to forge our futures together in San Francisco. Warner Brothers sponsored American Zoetrope for a short time, and with the money that it made available, I doled out fees to all, so that John could write *Apocalypse Now*, George could make *THX 1138*, and Carroll could write an original screenplay he called *Vesuvia*. About a year later, Warner Brothers rejected our entire slate of projects and later, when *The Godfather* became a success, demanded that I return all the development money it had laid out for the rejected projects, threatening to file an action to prevent me from making *The Godfather Part 2*. This was paid, and somehow I ended up owning all the scripts that had been written, including *Apocalypse Now*. I called George and let him know that I now owned the script and did he want to direct it. George said he was about to undertake a new science fiction project and wouldn't be able to get to *Apocalypse Now* for well over a year. Subsequently, I called John Milius and asked if he wanted to direct it, and John was also disposed on another project.

Then I thought that out of all the scripts I had ended up with, *Apocalypse Now* was the best one. Maybe if I directed it myself as a big action war film, American Zoetrope could make a lot of money, which we could use to make all of our small personal films. I thought, rather than make it on 16mm in Stockton, I'd like to make it in a huge format, even IMAX (which we investigated), and using Sensurround — make it *really* big. Anyway, I set off with my team and John Milius's script — finally selecting the Philippines as the best place to begin production.

However, when I made the film, instead of carrying the script day to day, I had a little green paperback of Conrad's *Heart of Darkness* in my pocket, filled with notes and markings. I just naturally started referring to it more than the script, and step by step, the film became more surreal and reminiscent of the great Conrad novella. However, I was painting myself into a corner. For the more I made it along the lines of Conrad, the less and less the original ending of John's script seemed to be appropriate. So every night I would feverishly rewrite the scenes for the next day, and each day the film I was shooting became stranger.

Many of the great scenes, memorable scenes, come verbatim from John Milius's original script: the set-up of the boat and those characters; the extraordinary helicopter assault playing Wagner through the loudspeakers; the tiger; the Playboy bunnies; and the weird Do Lung Bridge. My own work on the screenplay enhanced the Conrad parallel and augmented many of the scenes, including the French Plantation and most of the last act of the film. Dennis Hopper was originally hired to play Colby, the officer sent to assassinate Kurtz, only to become one of his subjects. But when I saw Dennis the first day, I dressed him up in a Montagnard shirt, put a bunch of cameras around his neck, and the crazed photojournalist somewhat based on rumors of Sean Flynn was born, and I lifted out of the pages of Conrad the character of the Russian who was there with Kurtz. Thus many people collaborated on the screenplay you are about to read, but most importantly of all John Milius, who is the original author, Michael Herr, who wrote the narration, and all of the actors, who in their improvisational work provided the basis of many of the scenes I would write out late at night.

FADE IN:

A SIMPLE IMAGE OF TREES—DAY

Coconut trees being VIEWED through the veil of time
or a dream. Occasionally colored smoke wafts through
the FRAME, yellow and then violet. MUSIC begins quietly, suggestive of 1968—69. Perhaps "The End" by the
Doors.

Now MOVING through the FRAME are skids of helicopters, not that we could make them out as that
though; rather, hard shapes that glide by at random. Then a phantom helicopter in FULL VIEW floats
by the trees—suddenly without warning, the jungle
BURSTS into a bright red-orange glob of napalm
flame.

The VIEW MOVES ACROSS the burning trees as the
smoke and ghostly helicopters come and go.

DISSOLVE TO:

INT. SAIGON HOTEL—DAY

A CLOSE SHOT, upside down of the stubble-covered
face of a young man. His EYES OPEN . . . this is B. L.
WILLARD. Intense and dissipated. The CAMERA MOVES
around to a side view as he continues to look up at
a ROTATING FAN on the ceiling.

IMAGES OF HELICOPTERS—DAY

They continue to fly slowly, peacefully across the burning jungle. The colored smoke comes and goes. Morrison continues with "The End."

INT. SAIGON HOTEL—DAY

The CAMERA MOVES slowly across the room . . . and we SEE WILLARD, a young army captain. He looks out the window to the busy Saigon street.

> **Willard (V.O.)**
> Saigon . . . shit. I'm still only in Saigon.
> Every time, I think I'm gonna wake up back
> in the jungle.

He moves back to the bed, lies down. He's unshaven, exhausted, probably drunk. We SEE alcohol bottles, photos, documents scattered on the table.

> **Willard (V.O.)**
> When I was home after my first tour, it was
> worse. I'd wake up and there'd be nothing. I
> hardly said a word to my wife until I said
> yes to a divorce. When I was here, I wanted
> to be there. When I was there . . . all I
> could think of was getting back into the
> jungle. I'm here a week now. Waiting for a
> mission. Getting softer. Every minute I stay
> in this room, I get weaker. And every min-
> ute Charlie squats in the bush . . . he gets
> stronger. Each time I looked around . . . the
> walls moved in a little tighter.

He's up now, naked, going into a frenzy, drinking, doing some sort of martial art, eventually collaps-ing onto the floor.

FADE IN:

INT. SAIGON HOTEL—STAIRWAY—DAY

Two extremely sharp army men walk up the stairs to Willard's room, a SERGEANT and a PRIVATE.

> **Willard (V.O.)**
> Everyone gets everything he wants. I wanted a mission. And for my sins, they gave me one. Brought it up to me like room service.

They knock on the door. A second knock.

> **Sergeant**
> Captain Willard, are you in there?

> **Willard (O.S.)**
> Yeah, I'm coming.

The army men wait for him.

> **Willard (V.O.)**
> It was a real choice mission. And when it was over, I'd never want another.

Willard unlocks the door and opens it. The men react to his condition.

> **Willard**
> What do you want?

> **Sergeant**
> Are you all right, Captain?

> **Willard**
> What's it look like?

Willard turns back into the room, sits on the bed.
The Sergeant follows him.

> **Sergeant**
> Are you Captain Willard? 505th Battalion?
> 173rd Air-borne? Assigned to SOG?

Willard looks over at the private by the door.

> **Willard**
> Hey, buddy, you gonna shut the door?

The private enters the room, closing the door behind him.

> **Sergeant**
> We have orders to escort you to the airfield.

> **Willard**
> What are the charges? What did I do?

> **Sergeant**
> There's no charges, Captain.

The sergeant opens the letter he has been holding.

> **Sergeant**
> You have orders to report to Com-Sec Intelli-
> gence at Nha Trang.

He holds up the letter in front of Willard's face
so he can see it. We see the word *Restricted* across
the top.

> **Willard**
> I see.

> **Sergeant**
> All right?

                          Willard
Nha Trang, for me?

                          Sergeant
That's right.

The sergeant folds the letter back up and puts it
back into the envelope. Willard doesn't move.

                          Sergeant
Come on, Captain, you still have a few hours
to get cleaned up.

                          Willard
I'm not feeling too good.

He lays his head on the pillow and closes his eyes.

                          Sergeant
Captain?
    (to private)
Dave, come here and give me a hand. We've got
a dead one.

The two of them move over to Willard and pick him up.

                     Sergeant (Cont'd)
Come on, Captain, let's go take a shower.

                          Willard
Don't be an ass.

                          Sergeant
    (to private)
Get hold of him good. We're going to take a
shower, Captain.

They drag him into the shower, and turn on the cold
water.

                    Sergeant (Cont'd)
    Stand under this, Captain.

Willard shudders and yells as they begin to clean
him up.

EXT. MILITARY COMPOUND—DAY

A darkly painted Huey lands in a guarded military
compound somewhere in Nha Trang. The two enlisted
men jump out of the helicopter, leading Willard,
who seems in much better shape. As he gets out he
sees a platoon of new men drilling in the hot hazy
sun. They are clean and pale.

                    Men (chanting)
    I wanna go to Vietnam.
    I wanna kill a Vietcong—

                    Willard (v.o.)
    I was going to the worst place in the world,
    and I didn't even know it yet. Weeks away
    and hundreds of miles up a river that snaked
    through the war like a circuit cable...
    plugged straight into Kurtz.

He follows the escort across the fields as the platoon drills.

                    Willard (V.O.) (Cont'd)
    It was no accident that I got to be the care-
    taker of Colonel Walter E. Kurtz's memory,
    any more than being back in Saigon was an
    accident. There is no way to tell his story
    without telling my own. And if his story is
    really a confession, then so is mine.

They approach a civilian-type luxury trailer. It is

surrounded by concertina wire, and its windows have grenade protection, but it still seems out of place in this austere military base.

CLOSER ON WILLARD

He stands before the door for a moment, as the MPs guarding the trailer check his papers.

INT. TRAILER—DAY

Cool and comfortable, furnished like a home. Pictures on the walls, certificates, photos of Presidents Kennedy, Johnson, and Nixon all in a row. There are Cambodian relics and other mementos decorating the room.

A small table is covered with linen and place settings for three.

Willard enters. He salutes, and the COLONEL salutes him back.

> **Colonel**
> *(to Willard)*
> Captain. Good. Come on in.

> **Willard**
> Thank you, sir.

> **Colonel**
> Stand at ease.

Willard notices somebody O.S. and reacts.

> **Willard**
> General.

The colonel crosses over to a cabinet and picks up a pack of cigarettes, as the CAMERA REVEALS a CIVILIAN; probably with the Department of Defense, sitting at the bar, and a GENERAL sitting on a sofa.

The colonel turns and offers Willard a cigarette from the pack.

> **Colonel**
> *(to Willard)*
> Do you want a cigarette?

> **Willard**
> No thank you, sir.

> **Colonel**
> *(indicating civilian)*
> Captain, have you ever seen this gentleman before?

> **Willard**
> No, sir. Not personally.

> **Colonel**
> You've worked a lot on your own, haven't you, Captain?

> **Willard**
> Yes, sir, I have.

> **Colonel**
> Your report specifies intelligence, counter-intelligence with Com-Sec, I Corps.

> **Willard**
> I'm not presently disposed to discuss those operations, sir.

There is a pause as the colonel lights his cigarette, then moves to the sofa. He bends down and
picks up a dossier, looks at it.

                    Colonel
Did you not work for the CIA in I Corps?

                    Willard
     (pause)
No, sir.

                    Colonel
Did you not assassinate a government tax
collector . . . Quang Tri province, June 18,
1968?

Willard doesn't answer.

                    Colonel
Captain?

                    Willard
Sir, I am unaware of any such activity or
operation, nor would I be disposed to dis-
cuss such an operation, if it did in fact
exist, sir.

A pause. Willard is tired and confused and hung
over, but he is handling himself well. The general
rises.

                    General
I thought we'd have a bit of lunch while we
talked. I hope you brought a good appetite,
Captain.

Willard gets up and moves toward the dining table
with the general and the civilian. They sit down

General (Cont'd)

I notice that you have a bad hand there. Are
you wounded?

Willard

Had a little fishing accident on R and R, sir.

General

Fishing on R and R?

Willard

Yes, sir.

General

But you're feeling fit? You're ready for duty?

Willard

Yes, General. Very much so, sir.

The food is being passed around.

General

Well, let's see what we have here. Roast
beef, and usually it's not bad.
  (to civilian)
Try some, Jerry. Pass it around. To save a
little time, we might pass both ways.
  (to Willard)
Captain, I don't know how you feel about
this shrimp, but if you eat it, you'll never
have to prove your courage in any other way.

The colonel, who is not eating with them, walks to
the table, holding a small photo.

Colonel

  (to Willard)
Captain, you've heard of Captain Walter E.
Kurtz?

He shows the photo to Willard.

INSERT THE PHOTO

It's an eight-by-ten black-and-white portrait of an
army officer wearing a beret.

                    Willard
        Yes, sir, I've heard the name.

The colonel accidentally drops the dossier. Papers,
photos, etc., scatter all over the floor. He stoops
down to pick them up.

                    Colonel
        Jesus . . . Operations officer, Fifth Special
        Forces.

                    General
        Luke, would you play that tape for the cap-
        tain, please?
          (to Willard)
        Listen to it carefully, Captain.

The colonel moves to a tape recorder and turns it on.

            Male Voice (On Tape) (V.O.)
        "October 9, 04:30 hours, Sector Peter, Victor,
        King."

                    General
        These were monitored out of Cambodia. It's
        been verified as Colonel Kurtz's voice.

All the men, including Willard, listen in wonder.

            Kurtz (On Tape) (V.O.)
        "I watched a snail, crawling on the edge of

a straight razor. That's my dream. It's my nightmare. Crawling, slithering, along the edge of a straight razor, and surviving."

Male Voice (On Tape) (V.O.)
"Transmission 11, received '68, December 30, 05:00 hours, Sector King, Zulu, King."

Kurtz (On Tape) (V.O.)
"But we must kill them. We must incinerate them. Pig after pig. Cow after cow. Village after village. Army after army. And they call me an assassin. What do you call it, when the assassins accuse the assassin? They lie. They lie and we have to be merciful, for those who lie. Those nabobs. I hate them. I really hate them."

The TAPE is TURNED OFF.

General
Walter Kurtz was one of the most outstanding officers this country's ever produced. He was brilliant. He was outstanding in every way. And he was a good man, too. A humanitarian man. A man of wit and humor. He joined the Special Forces, and after that, his ideas, methods, became . . . unsound. Unsound.

Colonel
Now he's crossed into Cambodia with this Montagnard army of his, that worship the man like a god, and follow every order, however ridiculous. Well, I have some other shocking news to tell you. Colonel Kurtz was about to be arrested for murder.

Willard
I don't follow, sir. Murdered who?

Colonel

Kurtz had ordered the execution of some Vietnamese intelligence agents. Men he believed were double agents. So he took matters into his own hands.

General

Well, you see, Willard, in this war, things get confused out there. Power, ideals, the old morality, and practical military necessity. But out there with these natives, it must be a temptation to be God. Because there's a conflict in every human heart between the rational and the irrational, between good and evil. And good does not always triumph. Sometimes, the dark side overcomes what Lincoln called the better angels of our nature. Every man has got a breaking point. You and I have them. Walter Kurtz has reached his. And, very obviously, he has gone insane.

Willard looks from the colonel to the general to the civilian. They are intensely interested in his response, which they want to be "yes."

Willard
(carefully)
Yes, sir. Very much so, sir. Obviously insane.

The three men pull back, satisfied.

Colonel

Your mission is to proceed up the Nung River in a navy patrol boat, pick up Colonel Kurtz's path at Nu Mung Ba, follow it, learn what you can along the way. When

you find the colonel, infiltrate his team
by whatever means available, and terminate
the colonel's command.

                    Willard
    (to General)
Terminate . . . the colonel?

                    General
He's out there operating without any decent
restraint, totally beyond the pale of any
acceptable human conduct. And he is still on
the field commanding troops.

                    Civilian
Terminate with extreme prejudice.

The civilian hands Willard a cigarette, and lights
it for him.

                    Colonel
You understand, Captain, that this mission
does not exist, nor will it ever exist.

CLOSE ON WILLARD

Smoking the cigarette, thinking about the mission.

                                        CUT TO:

EXT. THE MEKONG DELTA—DUSK

A HUEY helicopter flying over the mountains moves
over rice paddies, the Mekong River, MOVING CLOSER
until we view a dock area.

Willard (V.O.)

How many people had I already killed? There
were those six that I knew about for sure . . .
close enough to blow their last breath in my
face. But this time it was an American, and
an officer. That wasn't supposed to make any
difference to me, but it did.

We SEE a small patrol boat. It moves away from the
dock, out into the delta.

Willard (V.O.) (Cont'd)

Shit. Charging a man with murder in this
place was like handing out speeding tickets
at the Indy 500.

Willard (V.O.) (Cont'd)

I took the mission. What the hell else was I
gonna do? But I really didn't know what I'd
do when I found him.

EXT. PBR—DAY

We are CLOSE ON THE BOAT, the PBR. Willard is lying
on the deck, his eyes closed.

Willard (V.O.)

I was being ferried down the coast in a navy
PBR, a type of plastic patrol boat, pretty
common sight on the rivers. They said it was
a good way to pick up information, and move
without drawing a lot of attention. That was
okay. I needed the air and the time. Only
problem was, I wouldn't be alone.

Willard awakens to see a young black crewman squatting in front of him, brushing his teeth.

> **Willard (V.O.) (Cont'd)**
> The crew were mostly just kids. Rock 'n'
> rollers with one foot in their graves.
>   *(to Clean)*
> How old are you?

> **Clean**
> Seventeen.

VIEW ON CHEF, lanky, with a mustache.

> **Willard (V.O.)**
> The machinist, the one they called Chef, was
> from New Orleans. He was wrapped too tight
> for Vietnam. Probably wrapped too tight for
> New Orleans.

VIEW ON LANCE, blond, handsome, laid-back surfer
type. He is sunning himself with a reflector.

> **Willard (V.O.) (Cont'd)**
> Lance, from the forward 50's, was a famous
> surfer from the beaches south of L.A. To
> look at him, you wouldn't believe he'd ever
> fired a weapon in his life.

VIEW ON CLEAN, the young black man brushing his
teeth.

> **Willard (V.O.) (Cont'd)**
> Mr. Clean was from some South Bronx shit-
> hole, and I think the light and the space
> of Vietnam really put the zap on his head.

VIEW ON THE CHIEF, an older black man. He is at the
helm, studying a map of the delta.

> **Willard (V.O.) (Cont'd)**
> Then there was Phillips, the Chief. It might

have been my mission, but it sure as shit
was the Chief's boat.

> #### Chief
> (to Willard)
> There's about two points where we can draw
> enough water to get into the Nung River.
> They're both hot, belong to Charlie.

> #### Willard
> Don't worry about it.

He takes out a pack of cigarettes and offers one to
the Chief.

> #### Chief
> Don't smoke. You know, I've pulled a few
> special ops in here. About six months ago, I
> took a man who was going past the bridge at
> Do Lung. He was regular army, too. I heard
> he shot himself in the head.

Willard lights his cigarette as the boat continues
to move out into the ocean.

EXT. RIVER—THE PBR—DAY

Willard is sitting, smoking a cigarette, and looking down at a large pouch. He opens the flap and WE
SEE that there are several dossiers inside. He
opens one, thumbing through the material. We SEE
the personal letters, photographs, reports, files—
the entire case history of Colonel Walter E. Kurtz.

> #### Willard (V.O.)
> At first, I thought they handed me the
> wrong dossier. I couldn't believe they
> wanted this man dead. Third-generation

West Point, top of his class . . . Korea, Airborne, about a thousand decorations, etc., etc. I'd heard his voice on the tape and it really put the hook in me, but I couldn't connect up that voice with this man. Like they said, he had an impressive career. Maybe too impressive. I mean, perfect. He was being groomed for one of the top slots in the corporation. General, chief of staff, anything. In 1964, he returned from a tour with Advisory Command in Vietnam, and things started to slip. His report to the Joint Chiefs of Staff and Lyndon Johnson was restricted. Seems they didn't dig what he had to tell them. During the next few months, he made three requests . . . for transfer to Airborne training, Fort Benning, Georgia . . . and was finally accepted. Airborne? He was thirty-eight years old. Why the fuck would he do that? 1966 . . . joins Special Forces, returns to Vietnam.

Suddenly we HEAR a sound, a distant EXPLOSION. The crew all stop whatever they are doing, look out beyond the shore and the green jungled hills. There is a distant ROLLING NOISE, like interrupted thunder. The buffeting and the noise continue.

Chef

What's that?

Willard

Arc light.

Lance

What's up?

                    Willard
B-52 strike.

                     Chef
What's that?

                    Willard
Arc light!

                     Chef
I hate that. Every time I hear that, something terrible happens.

                     Clean
Charlie don't never see them or hear them,
man.

                     Lance
There they are!

He points up to the sky.

EXT. SKY—FULL SHOT—DAY

Way up—past any clouds and barely discernible—
we SEE the black silhouettes of four B-52 bombers,
their vapor trails streaming white against the dark
blue sky.

                     Clean
Concussion'll suck the air out of your damn
lungs.

                     Chef
Something terrible is going to happen.

                         Clean
              Smoke! Secondary burning.

FULL SHOT—COASTLINE

Black smoke rises from the jungle.

                         Chief
              Hueys over there. Lots of Hueys.

                         Willard
              Let's have a look, Chief.

The Chief hands Willard the field glasses. He looks
through them out at the burning coastline.

                  Willard (V.O.) (Cont'd)
              It was the Air-Cav, First of the Ninth.
                (to Chief)
              That's them.

All the crew move to battle positions, get their
flak jackets, helmets, etc.

                  Willard (V.O.) (Cont'd)
              Our escorts to the mouth of the Nung
              River. But they were supposed to be waiting
              for us another thirty kilometers ahead.
              Well, Air Mobile. Those boys just couldn't
              stay put.

The PBR moves to the beach through a chaos of other
boats, low-flying helicopters, and soldiers rushing
by onshore.

EXT. BEACH AND VILLAGE—DAY

A vast field of devastation, smashed and burning
huts, shattered sampans and bodies washing around
in the surf. Willard jumps off the boat, Clean
and Lance fall in behind him, and they head
ashore.

> **Willard (V.O.)**
> First of the Ninth was an old cavalry
> division that had cashed in its horses
> for choppers, and gone tear-assing around
> Nam looking for the shit. They'd given
> Charlie a few surprises in their time
> here. What they were mopping up now hadn't
> even happened yet an hour ago.

They make their way across the beach, weapons in
hand. Explosions go off around them; there is smoke
everywhere. Suddenly they are stopped by a VOICE.

> **Voice (O.S.)**
> Go on, keep going. It's for television.
> Don't look at the camera.

Willard and the two who are following stop incred-
ulously, their M16s still in hand.

> **Voice (O.S.)**
> Go on, go on, keep going. Don't look at the
> camera.

REVERSE ANGLE ON WHAT THEY SEE

A NEWS TEAM, dressed in fatigues and combat dress.
A director, cameraman, and soundman; the director
keeps waving them by.

> **Director (to Troops)**
> Just go by like you're fighting. Don't look

at the camera. It's for television. Just
go through. Just go by. Keep on going.

Willard, Lance, and Clean run by, staring into the
camera the entire time.

They make their way toward the village under siege.
Willard stops to talk with a SERGEANT, as a medevac
helicopter takes off in the background. The Hueys
and Loches in the sky drown out most of their conversation.

CLOSE ON WILLARD

looking up as the Hueys sweep in low.

> **Willard**
> Where can I find the CO?

> **Sergeant**
> That's the colonel coming down!

He points to a particular Huey in the sky, and
moves to a clear spot by a large bomb crater. He
takes out a smoke bomb and pulls the pin and lays
it down in the clearing, as it spews out orange
smoke.

> **Willard**
> *(to his men)*
> CO's on that chopper.

Willard moves back to Lance and Clean, they all
kneel, trying to avoid the propeller wash, as they
look up.

FULL VIEW

The helicopter is heavily laden with machine guns, etc., as it lands in the middle of the clearing.

A tall, strong-looking man jumps out of the helicopter. This is COLONEL WILLIAM KILGORE. He puts on his Air-Cav hat, managing to do it against the rotor wash, then stands to his full immense height and with his hands on his hips, surveys the field of battle.

                    Kilgore
    Lieutenant, bomb that tree line back about
    a hundred yards. Give me some room to
    breathe.

                    Lieutenant
    Yes, sir!

Kilgore starts walking, then turns and shouts to the LIEUTENANT.

                    Kilgore
    Bring my body cards!

                    Lieutenant
    Yes, sir!

The lieutenant moves back to the helicopter and Kilgore continues forward toward the besieged village. A CAPTAIN from the tank division comes running down the street, stops in front of Kilgore.

                    Captain
    I'm the Fourth Tank commander. I've got five
    tanks broken down.

Kilgore

All right with the tanks. It's all right, Captain.

The captain turns and exits, as the sergeant walks up leading Willard, Lance, and Clean.

Willard

Captain Willard.

They exchange salutes. Willard takes out a set of orders and hands them to him.

Willard

I carry priority papers from Com-Sec Intelligence, II Corps! I understand Nha Trang has briefed you on the requirements of my mission!

Kilgore

What mission? I haven't heard from Nha Trang.

Kilgore hands the orders to the major, who has joined him. He looks at them and shakes his head "no."

Willard

Sir, you're supposed to escort us into the Nung!

The major hands the orders back to Willard. By this time the lieutenant has run back in from the helicopter with the deck of playing cards. He hands them to Kilgore.

Kilgore

We'll see what we can do about that! Just stay out of my way till this is done, Captain!

Kilgore cracks the plastic wrapping sharply, takes the deck of new cards and fans them. Then he strides past Willard and his two young crewmen with no further acknowledgment—the others follow.

He moves through the shell-pocked field of devastation, soldiers gathering around him. As he comes to each V.C. corpse, he drops a card on it, carefully picking out which card he uses.

> **Kilgore**
> *(to himself)*
> All right, let's see what we have. Two of spades. Three of spades. Four of diamonds, six of clubs . . . There isn't one worth a jack in the whole bunch. Four of diamonds...

He crosses on down the street, distributing his cards on top of the dead V.C. corpses.

Willard, Lance, and Clean have been following Kilgore. Willard bends down and picks up one of the cards from a dead V.C.

> **Lance**
> Hey, Captain, what's that?

> **Willard**
> Death cards.

> **Lance**
> What?

> **Willard**
> Death cards. Lets Charlie know who did this.

MOVING SHOT ON KILGORE

as he moves through the corpses, selecting a card and flipping it on a body, or putting it behind an ear.

                    Kilgore
        (to a shell-shocked G.I.)
    Cheer up, son.

As they pass by a well, two G.I.s jump out of it.

                      G.I.
    Fire in the hole!

The all hit the deck, as a tremendous explosion comes out of the well.

Kilgore, his lieutenant, and major stop in back of a large gathering of villagers. They are standing around a G.I. and ARVN Interpreter, listening to them.

              Soldier (Over P.A.)
    This is an area that's controlled by the Vietcong and North Vietnamese! We are here to help you! We are here to extend a welcome hand to those of you who would like to return to the arms of the South Vietnamese government.

A line of villagers are throwing all their belongs on top of a large APC parked by the road, and filing into the carrier. Kilgore stops and watches the G.I.s help them, then he moves over and looks at the inside, where the villagers are crowded together, waiting and scared.

                    Kilgore
        (to woman)
    Get in! Hurry up!

> (to soldier)

Move it out!

Soldier (Over P.A.)
This is an area that is controlled by the Vietcong and North Vietnamese . . .

Kilgore turns and continues down the burning street with his group. He comes upon a wounded V.C., groaning. The man has tied a wash bowl over his belly—and is groaning for water. Kilgore turns to a soldier.

Kilgore
What's this?

Soldier (Over P.A.)
This man's hurt pretty bad, sir. About the only thing holding his guts in, sir, is that pot lid.

Kilgore
> (to ARVN soldier)

Yeah? What does he have to say?

ARVN Soldier
This soldier is dirty V.C. He wants water. He can drink paddy water.

Kilgore
Get out of here! Give me that canteen.

He pushes the ARVN soldier away, turns, and gets a canteen full of water from the lieutenant.

Kilgore
Any man who's brave enough to fight—

Kilgore

(to ARVN soldier)

Get outta here! I'll kick your fucking ass!
Any man brave enough to fight with his guts
strapped on him can drink from my canteen
any day.

He stoops down—starts to quench the prisoner's thirst
from his canteen. A soldier rushes up to him.

Soldier

Colonel, I think one of those sailors is
Lance Johnson, the surfer.

Kilgore

Where? Here? You sure?

The soldier points at Lance.

Soldier

Down there.

Kilgore rises, hands the canteen back, and moves
over to Willard and his crew. Looks at Lance.

Willard

What's your name, sailor?

Lance

(salutes)

Gunner's Mate Third Class L. Johnson, sir!

Kilgore

Lance Johnson the surfer?

Lance

Yes, sir.

Kilgore smiles, sticks out his hand.

Kilgore

Well, it's an honor to meet you, Lance. I've
admired your nose riding for years. Your cutback, too. I think you have the best cutback
there is.

Lance

Thank you, sir.

Kilgore

You can cut out the 'sir' crap, Lance. I'm
Bill Kilgore. I'm a 'goofy foot.'

Kilgore leads Lance off to meet some other soldiers. Willard's entire top-priority mission has
been put in the background.

Kilgore
(making introductions)
I want you to meet some guys. This is Mike
from San Diego. Johnny from Malibu. We're
pretty solid surfers. None of us are anywhere near your class, though.

Mike

No way.

Lance shakes their hands. Kilgore moves on, the
group follows him.

Kilgore

We do a lot of surfing around here, Lance.
I like to finish operations early, fly down
to Yung Tau for the evening glass. Been
riding since you got here?

Lance

No way. I haven't surfed since I been
here.

They stop; we see a Catholic Mass going on in the middle of a graveyard. Many helicopters continue to hover overhead. Willard looks around him, looks at the Mass being held, as the priest continues from his altar on a gravestone in the midst of the bombing and evacuations.

EXT. AREA BY DESTROYED VILLAGE—NIGHT

The area is illuminated by large cans filled with sand and jet fuel, bonfires, and the burning village in the background. There are maybe fifteen to twenty helicopters secured against the wind, in orderly patterns. Men are grouped around the fires, eating steaks, hot dogs, hamburgers, drinking beer. It has the bizarre resemblance to some sort of barbarian beach party.

> **Willard (V.O.)**
> Kilgore'd had a pretty good day for himself.
> They choppered in the T-bones and the beer
> . . . and turned the L.Z. into a beach party.
> The more they tried to make it just like
> home, the more they made everybody miss it.

Kilgore is seated at a fire with some of his men, strumming a guitar and singing.

> **Kilgore**
> *(to the Chef)*
> Make my meat rare. Rare but not cold.

> **Willard (V.O.)**
> Well, he wasn't a bad officer, I guess. He
> loved his boys, and you felt safe with him.
> He was one of those guys that had that weird
> light around him. You just knew he wasn't
> going to get so much as a scratch here.

Kilgore looks at Willard, who more or less sits by
himself.

Kilgore
What happened to your mission, Captain? Nha
Trang forget all about you?

He laughs. Willard gets up, carrying the map he's
patiently been holding. He lays it down in front of
Kilgore; squats and points.

Willard
Sir, two places we can get into the river.
Here and here. It's a pretty wide delta, but
these are the only two spots I'm really sure
of.

Kilgore
That village you're pointing at is kind of
hairy, Willard.

Willard
What do mean "hairy," sir?

Kilgore
It's hairy. Got some pretty heavy ordinance.
I've lost a few recon ships in there now and
again.

The Chief comes over, leans in to take a look at
the map.

Kilgore
What's the name of that goddamn village,
Vin Drin Dop or Lop? Damn gook names all
sound the same.
   (to one of the surfer soldiers)
Mike, you know anything about this point at
Vin Drin Dop?

                    Mike
That's a fantastic peak.

                  Kilgore
Peak?

                    Mike
About six foot. It's an outstanding peak.
It's got both the long right and left
slide, with a bowl section that's unbelievable. It's just tube city.

Kilgore considers this.

                  Kilgore
Well, why didn't you tell me that before? A
good peak. There aren't any good peaks in
this whole shitty country. It's all goddamn
beach break.

                    Mike
It's really hairy in there, sir. That's
where we lost McDonald. They shot the hell
out of us there. That's Charlie's Point.

Willard sees his chance, jumps in.

                  Willard
Sir, we could go in there tomorrow at dawn.
There's always a good offshore breeze in
the morning.

The Chief is doubtful.

                   Chief
We may not be able to get the boat in. The
draft at the mouth of that river may be too
shallow.

The colonel rises, looks at Willard.

                    Kilgore
We'll pick your boat up and put it down
like a baby, right where you want it. This
is the First of the Ninth, Air-Cav, son.
Air mobile! I can take that point and hold
it just as long as I like, and you can get
any place up that river that suits you,
young Captain. Hell, a six-foot peak! All
right. Take a gunship back to the division.
   (to Lance)
Lance, go with Mike and let him pick out a
board for you. And bring me my Yater Spoon,
the eight-six.

Mike reacts, doubtful.

                    Kilgore
What is it, soldier?

                    Mike
It's pretty hairy in there. It's Charlie's
Point.

Kilgore looks at him, exasperated.

                    Kilgore
Charlie don't surf!

                                        CUT TO:

**EXT. HELICOPTER FIELD OUTSIDE DESTROYED
VILLAGE—DAY**

It is the next morning. The helicopters, pilots,
and men are ready for battle. The helicopters
slowly start up, as the soldiers scurry about to
their various positions.

We FOLLOW Kilgore and his group, including Willard, the Chief, Clean, Lance, etc., as they walk across the field. They all get into the helicopters, except Kilgore. He takes off his hat, reaches in, and pulls out his helmet, puts it on.

ANGLE ON OUR CREW

seated in their helicopter, looking out.

> **Chef**
> Jesus, Clean, you ain't gonna believe this. Look.

WHAT THEY SEE:

The PBR being airlifted up by a helicopter.

> **Clean**
> Hey! They're picking up the boat!

BACK TO KILGORE'S HELICOPTER

Kilgore picks up some gloves and starts to put them on as he crosses to the gunner by the helicopter.

> **Kilgore**
> *(to soldier)*
> How you feeling, Jimmy?

> **Soldier**
> Like a mean motherfucker, sir!

Kilgore
(to bugler)
All right, son, let 'er rip

The bugler begins to play as Kilgore climbs into the helicopter.

EXTREME FULL SHOT

THE HELICOPTERS take off, rotors spinning, gas turbines belching fire from their jet pipes, sand and dust flying as twenty helicopters RISE.

NOISE ROAR OVER CAMERA. The helicopters deploy into a formation.

NEW VIEWS—HELICOPTERS

They move THROUGH THE FRAME, almost a dance of dragonflies.

INT. COMMAND COPTER—MED. SHOT—KILGORE, WILLARD, OTHERS

Willard looks ahead, Kilgore sits near the door. Below, they see the jungle whisk by and are suddenly over the ocean, low and fast.

MONTAGE—CLOSE SHOTS OF ROCKET PODS WITH MINIGUNS

In their bizarre-looking mounts as well as the men—young, anticipating, holding their rifles, looking down.

CLOSE ON WILLARD—HIS POV

looking out from the side door. The various troop ships moving by. The men waiting, sitting on the floor, sitting on their helmets, looking back at him.

FULL VIEW OF THE HELICOPTERS

They are magnificent in the sky as they split into two columns.

INSIDE HELICOPTER

Kilgore cranes his neck and leans out to watch the waves, then he turns back to Lance.

> **Kilgore**
> I never have got used to a light board. I can't get used to one. I'm used to a heavy board.

> **Lance**
> I know, it's a real drag.

> **Kilgore**
> You prefer a heavy or a light board?

> **Lance**
> Heavier.

> **Kilgore**
> Really?

> **Lance**
> Yeah.

Kilgore
I thought young guys like lighter boards.

Lance
Can't ride the nose on those things.

The pilot alerts the colonel.

Pilot
(to Kilgore)
Duke Six, this is Eagle Thrust Seven. We've got it spotted.

Kilgore
Eagle Thrust, put on heading two-seven-zero, assume attack formation.

Pilot
That's a Roger, Big Duke. We're going in hot. Here we go.

Kilgore
(to Lance)
We'll come in low out of the rising sun, and about a mile out, we'll put on the music.

Lance
Music?

Kilgore
Yeah, I use Wagner. Scares the hell out of the slopes. My boys love it.

Lance
(to Willard)
Hey, they're gonna play music!

INT. PBR CREW'S COPTER—DAY

As they get near the destination, several of the soldiers take off their helmets and sit on them. The PBR crew reacts with surprise.

> **Chef**
> How come all you guys sit on your helmet?

> **Soldier**
> So we don't get our balls blown off.

Chef laughs, looks around. Then he takes off his own helmet and sits on it.

INT. COMMAND COPTER—DAY

VIEW ON KILGORE

> **Kilgore**
> *(to pilot)*
> Eagle Thrust, put on psy war op. Make it loud.
> This is a Romeo Fox Trot. Shall we dance?

A HAND switches on the tape deck. MUSIC COMES UP, Wagner's "Ride of the Valkyrie," blaring through the external speakers of the choppers, as they make their descent into enemy territory.

EXT. THE COMMAND HELICOPTER

with enormous twelve-driver loudspeakers BLASTING out the music.

INT. PBR CREW'S COPTER

Our crew is silent, nervous.

EXT. COPTERS—DAY

We SEE the bombs and a surfboard attached to the bottom of the helicopters.

EXT. VIETCONG VILLAGE—FULL SHOT

Typical quiet Vietnamese coastal village, rather large, built along the beach and trees with rice paddies behind. Sampans are pulled into a cove where they are being unloaded. We SEE different aspects of the life of the village, the people working there.

MED. SHOT—SCHOOLYARD

A teacher and a little girl come out into the courtyard, quickly followed by other students pouring from the schoolhouse in the background. A North Vietnamese soldier runs in to the teacher, who then turns back to the children. The soldier waves to the children to get out of the area.

CLOSER ON THE TEACHER

gathering children together. Peasants run through as the teacher starts the children running out. One small boy remains, an older girl runs back to get him and run after the others.

Soon the village is buzzing with activity. Trenches are used to pass weapons and ammunitions, young V.C.—both men and women. NVA regulars rush along the trenches to take their positions.

NEW VIEW—NVA AND V.C.

rushing along the trenches and taking the camou-flage covering off a large automatic antiaircraft weapon.

EXT. THE SKY—NEW VIEW

moving behind an assault column of helicopters.

INT. COMMAND COPTER

Kilgore monitoring the transmission.

CLOSE VIEW ON WILLARD

watching the spectacle.

CLOSE VIEW ON KILGORE

calm and very effective. Seems almost like an astronaut. Willard looks down at this incredible battle.

WILLARD'S POV—AERIAL VIEW—THE VILLAGE

The village under attack. The invincible cavalry charges in, hurling all its fearful weaponry, blasting out the Wagner.

INT. POV BEHIND PILOT

                    Pilot
          (to Kilgore)
     We've spotted a large weapon down below.
     We're gonna go down and check it out.

The helicopter shakes as we SEE the smoke of the rocket shoot ahead of us.

REVERSE

A Vietnamese house goes up in flame.

MED. CLOSE—GUN SHIP

sweeping down, its miniguns FIRING. V.C. scatter.

INT. COMMAND COPTER

                    Kilgore
     Outstanding, Red Team.
          (to pilot)
     Get you a case of beer for that one.

COPTER'S POV ON SQUARE—HIGH ANGLE

Watching Vietnamese loading ammunition into an old Citroën car. The copter circles over them.

Pilot #1
We're over the village right now. I think I see a vehicle down in the courtyard. I'm gonna check it out.

Kilgore
Well done, Hawks. Well done. Want some twenty-Mike-Mike-Vulcan right along those treelines. Ripple the shit out of them.

Pilot #2
Got a vehicle on the bridge, fifty caliber on-board. He's moving across to resupply weapon.

Kilgore
Big Duke Six. Clear the area. I'm coming down myself.
(to himself)
Don't these people ever give up?

VIEW—THE COMMAND COPTER

It circles the area. Gunships hit the Citroën that's trying to cross the bridge. The car bursts into flame and the ammunition is EXPLODED.

Lance
(to Kilgore)
Nice shot, Bill!

The copter suddenly lurches over to the right. The ship is jostled around badly. There are some flames and smoke and it looks as though the copter has been seriously hit. There is confu-

sion and we realize that the bullets have hit a
box of flares which have gone off inside the
copter.

Kilgore
(to soldiers)
Un-ass that shit and get it out of here! It's
just a flare, it's all right, it's just a flare.
Everybody all right? Lance, you all right?

Lance
I'm fine!

EXT. VILLAGE—COPTERS LANDING

A small group of copters come down and land, kicking up clouds of dust. Soldiers start to jump off,
run for cover, as shells hit the ground. All jump
out except for one YOUNG SOLDIER.

Young Soldier
I'm not going! I'm not going! I'm not
going!

Another soldier comes back, grabs him by the arm,
and pulls him out of copter.

NEW VIEW—AMERICANS ON THE GROUND

proceed in driving the V.C. from the village, firing
into houses. One soldier fires his rifle into a row
of storage jars in front of a house. They explode.
A black soldier is thrown by the blast.

Soldier (Over Radio)
We got some secondaries down there in the
plaza.

                    Soldier #2 (Over Radio)
Hold onto your positions.

                    Soldier (Over Radio)
Duke Six, Duke Six. We've got wounded down
there.

VIEW ON THE COURTYARD

Soldiers huddle around the severely wounded black
G.I., who is screaming out. The RT man is frantically calling for a medevac as two Vietnamese
elders babble on for their lives, explaining that
they didn't know the booby trap was near their
house.

                        Medic
Get a stretcher over here!

                    Wounded Soldier
Please, God, help me!

                        Medic
Let's give him some morphine.

                    Soldier (Over Radio)
Zero-three-seven-seven-four-two.

                        Medic
Where's that duster?

INT. COMMAND COPTER

Kilgore looking out the door as he flies from the
river down over the courtyard.

Kilgore
(into radio)
I want my wounded out of there and in the hospital in fifteen minutes. I want my men out.

COPTER'S POV OF COURTYARD

Soldier (Over Radio)
Somebody stand tight there with Big Duke.

Soldier #2 (Over Radio)
This is Ten-Ten, we're going to be in there and get out.

EXT. THE COURTYARD

as a medevac helicopter comes down landing by the smoke. They carry the wounded G.I. into the helicopter.

Frantic Americans push the two older Vietnamese into the medevac ship for questioning. A YOUNG VIETNAMESE WOMAN suddenly rushes out from one of the buildings, making a fuss about the older Vietnamese. Then she throws her coolie hat into the open helicopter door.

Soldier
She's got a grenade! She's got a grenade!

Everyone scatters.

EXT. HELICOPTER—HIGH VIEW

Helicopter BLOWS into flame. Men rush out on fire. They frantically try to put themselves out.

INT. COMMAND COPTER

Looking down on the burning helicopter.

>   **Pilot**
> They blew the shit out of it.

>   **Kilgore**
> Fucking savages.

>   **Copilot**
> Holy Christ, she's a SAP. I'm gonna get that dink bitch. Get over there, Johnny. Put the right skid right up her ass.

MED. VIEW—THE HELICOPTER

It swerves down. We can SEE the disaster as well as the three Vietnamese running away. It ROARS down, the machine gunner FIRING.

VIEW ON THE GROUND

The Vietnamese are mowed down.

OVER-THE-SHOULDER SHOT OF THE TREES BELOW THE COPTER

Shells are fired from the grove of trees at the copter.

Pilot (Over Radio)
We gotta get some air up in these trees.
It's goddamn eat-up with enemy down there.

The LOH swerves past the tree line taking sniper
FIRE and finally a dead-on HIT. It swerves around in
circles, black smoke coming from it, cascading
toward the ground.

Copters fire at the bridge. Smoke and debris fly
upward. Geysers of water almost obscure it. The
bridge is destroyed, the village burns in the background.

INT. COMMAND COPTER

Kilgore turns to look at Lance.

                    Kilgore
        What do you think?

                    Lance
        It's really exciting, man.

                    Kilgore
        No, no! The waves!

                    Lance
        Oh, right.

                    Kilgore
        Look at that, breaks both ways. Watch. Look!
        Good six-foot swells!

EXT. BEACH—DAY

Kilgore's copter kicks up a cloud of dust as it
sets down. Kilgore pops out, followed by Lance and
other officers and strides across the beach looking
out toward the sea.

> Soldier (O.S.)
Incoming!

They all dive except Kilgore; he's watching a big
set. The shell EXPLODES in the water about a hundred yards away, sending up a geyser of spray.
Kilgore is unmoved. The others get up and join
him.

> Major
This L.Z. is still pretty hot, sir. Maybe
you ought to surf somewhere else.

> Kilgore
What do you know about surfing, Major?
You're from goddamn New Jersey!

He whistles Mike and Johnny over, who look like
they're ready to hit the dirt again as explosions
go off around them.

> Kilgore
Come here! Come here! Change.

> Mike
You mean right now, sir?

> Kilgore
I wanna see how rideable that stuff is.
Go change.

> Mike
It's still pretty hairy out there, sir.

> **Kilgore**
> You wanna surf, soldier?

They nod "yes" meekly.

> **Kilgore**
> That's good son, because you either surf or
> fight. That clear?

They turn and leave. Kilgore grabs an M16 from one
of the guards—they all think he's going to shoot
the surfers or someone—they run back uneasy.

> **Kilgore**
> Now get going. I'll cover for them.
> *(to others)*
> And bring a board for Lance.

He cocks the weapon—Lance looks around uneasily.

> **Willard**
> *(to Lance)*
> We can't do shit till the boat gets here.

> **Kilgore**
> Lance, I bet you can't wait to get out there.

> **Lance**
> What?

> **Kilgore**
> *(gesturing to ocean)*
> See how they break both ways? One guy can
> break right, one left, simultaneous. What do
> you think of that?

> **Lance**
> Bill, I think we ought to wait for the tide
> to come up.

He starts away.

> ### Kilgore
> Lance, come here. Look.

> ### Soldier (O.S.)
> Incoming!

A shell screams over—they all hit the dirt except Kilgore. It explodes, throwing sand through the air. Kilgore leans down yelling over the noise.

> ### Kilgore
> The tide doesn't come in for six hours! You wanna wait here for six hours?

ANGLE ON THE PBR

in the sky, being dropped by the helicopter onto the water.

MED. SHOT—SURF—THE TWO SURFERS

out on the water on their boards, trying to surf.

> ### Kilgore (O.S.)
> *(through megaphone)*
> Okay, fellas, quit hiding. Let's go, dick-heads, take off.

ANGLE ON KILGORE, HOLDING A MEGAPHONE

watching the surfers. JETS SCREAM overhead, FIRING CANNONS. Helicopters wheel by carrying out wounded.

Willard

Goddamnit! Don't you think it's a little risky for R and R?

Kilgore

If I say it's safe to surf this beach, Captain, it's safe to surf this beach! I mean, I'm not afraid to surf this place! I'll surf this fucking place!

He rips off his shirt and scarf.

Kilgore
(to soldier)
Give me that R-T, soldier.
(into radio)
Dove Four, this is Big Duke Six. Goddamnit, I want that tree line bombed!

Bomber Pilot (Over Radio)

Big Duke Six, Roger. Dove One-Three, stand by.

Kilgore (O.S.)
(into radio)
Bomb them into the stone age, son.

He throws the R-T back to a soldier. We SEE from among the Vietnamese prisoners being herded, a woman running, covered with blood, carrying a bloody baby. She is trying to offer it up to the colonel, but a soldier is dutifully trying to keep her away from him.

Soldier

No, ma'am, no!

Kilgore

Let me take care of this now.

>   *(indicates soldier's rifle)*
>   Get that out of here!

Kilgore intercedes, pushing the soldier's rifle
away.

>   **Kilgore**
>   *(to woman)*
>   Come here now. All right. Sorry, you can't
>   go!

He takes the wounded baby in his hands, tenderly,
and calls a soldier over.

>   **Kilgore**
>   Jimmy!

ANGLE ON "LOC" SPOTTER PLANE IN THE SKY

>   **LOC (Over Radio)**
>   Hawk One-Two, Dove One-Three. They need some
>   napalm down there. Can you put it there?

>   **Fighter Pilot (Over Radio)**
>   Right, One-Three. We're fixed to fuck with
>   them.

>   **LOC (Over Radio)**
>   Trying to suppress some mortar fire off the
>   tree line down there.

>   **Fighter Pilot (Over Radio)**
>   Roger. Here we come.

>   **LOC (Over Radio)**
>   Good. Give it all you got and bring in all
>   your ships. Wing abreast.

> **Kilgore**
> *(to Jimmy)*
> Tell them to get my chopper, get back to the
> hospital.

He hands the baby to the soldier. Woman protests.

> **Kilgore**
> No, no no. You've got to go with him. Go! Go!
> *(to soldier)*
> Get it out of here! And tell my guys I want
> my board!

> **LOC (Over Radio)**
> Big Duke Six, this is Dove One-Three. The
> jets are inbound now. They got about thirty
> seconds to bomb station. Get your people
> back. This is gonna be a big one.

Kilgore returns to Lance, who is cowering in a fox-
hole with Willard.

> **Kilgore**
> Don't worry. We'll have this place cleaned
> up in a jiffy, son. Give me those shorts.

He turns to his aide, who hands him a pair of Air-
Cav trunks.

> **Kilgore**
> *(to Lance)*
> These are from the Air-Cav, a present from
> me and the boys. I wanna see you do your
> stuff out there.

Jets break the trees, we HEAR the EXPLOSION of 20-
mm CANNONS, and then the entire tree line ERUPTS
INTO FIRE with an immense amount of napalm.

Kilgore stands there, hands on hips, looking at the burning jungle in the distance.

                    Kilgore
You smell that? Do you smell that?

                    Lance
What?

                    Kilgore
       (pointing to trees)
Napalm, son. Nothing else in the world smells like that.
       (crouches down)
I love the smell of napalm in the morning. You know, one time we had a hill bombed for twelve hours . . . and when it was all over, I walked up. We didn't find one of them, not one stinking dink body. The smell, you know that gasoline smell? The whole hill—smelled like—victory.

He looks off nostalgically. A shell comes in and HITS in the background. Willard and the soldiers react; Kilgore ignores it.

                    Kilgore
Someday this war's gonna end.

A tremendous sadness enveloping him. Then he stands up and walks off. Willard turns and looks toward him. He understands what the colonel is saying to him.

ANGLE—KILGORE—WALKING OUT TOWARD THE SURF

Suddenly he senses something. He stops, lifts his hand—then licks his fingers and puts them in the air.

Kilgore

(to Lance)

Lance! The wind! The wind! It's blowing onshore! It's gonna blow this place out. It's gonna ruin it!

Sure enough, there is a rushing breeze that increases.

Lance

Not cool!

Kilgore

It's the goddamn napalm, that's what's doing it!

Willard

I'm really sorry, Colonel, but I'm afraid that does it. The kid's got a reputation. You can't expect him to surf those sloppy waves.

Kilgore

I understand what you're saying.

Lance

Yeah, I'm an artist, Bill. I couldn't surf that crap.

MED. VIEW—KILGORE, WILLARD, LANCE

Willard calmly goes about picking up Lance's clothes as Kilgore apologizes to Lance for the conditions.

Kilgore

Look, I apologize. It's not my fault. The waves are getting blown out by the napalm. It's the bombs causing a vortex with the wind.

                    Lance
I accept your apology.

                    Kilgore
Hang around just twenty minutes.

                    Willard
Some other time, Bill.

                    Kilgore
Just twenty minutes!

Willard grabs Lance and walks him away from Kilgore.

                    Lance
I'm an artist!

                    Willard
     (to Lance)
Keep walking.

Kilgore takes the megaphone.

                    Kilgore
     (into megaphone to surfers)
Let's give it a try, guys. One goes left and
one goes right.
     (to Lance)
Look, Lance . . .

Lance and Willard keep walking, fast.

                    Willard
You through surfing? Wanna say good-bye to
the colonel?

                    Lance
No!

>   **Willard**
> You sure?

>   **Lance**
> Yeah!

>   **Willard**
> Then let's get the fuck out of here!

Kilgore is left frantic on the beach with his megaphone.

>   **Kilgore**
>   *(calling to them)*
>   Lance, it's the fucking napalm! Just wait
>   twenty minutes! Fuck!

Willard and Lance run like hell toward the PBR in the distance. In his frustration, Kilgore throws the megaphone in the air and wanders off.

AT THE PBR

The crew help Willard and Lance climb onto the boat. Suddenly Willard sees something and stops. In a pile of equipment that the Hueys have left are two surfboards—Willard looks at them.

>   **Willard**
>   *(to PBR)*
>   Don't leave without me!

>   **Clean**
> Where the fuck are you going?

He runs to the copter where Kilgore's surfboard is attached.

                              Willard
        Incoming!

All the soldiers at the copter duck and during that
moment, Willard snatches the colonel's surfboard. A
soldier tries to stop him.

                         Soldier
        That's the colonel's surfboard!

                         Willard
        Get the fuck off me! It's mine!

He rushes back to the boat, handing the board up
to Clean, and scampers aboard. Clean stuffs the
board in the stern. The boat turns, ENGINES RUN-
NING HARD AND ROARS OFF toward the deeper water of
the river.

MED. CLOSE SHOT—WILLARD

on the bow: laughing, exhausted, feeling satisfied
with himself.

EXT. VILLAGE—DAY

The PBR passes the burned-out village, through the
destroyed bridge, and heads out toward the river.

EXT. PBR—DAY

The crew is relaxing. Clean sits down next to Chef,
who is rolling a joint.

                         Clean
        Chef, light up, man. Come on, let's get high.

Chef

(to Lance)
Wanna smoke?

Clean

Light up.

Willard (V.O.)

Someday this war's gonna end. That'd be just fine with the boys on the boat. They weren't looking for anything more than a way home.

Chef

Captain?

Chef offers the joint to Willard. He waves it off.

Willard (V.O.)

Trouble is, I'd been back there . . . and I knew that it just didn't exist anymore.

Lance

(to group)
Buddha time.

The crew shares the joint.

Clean

All right. That's grass. That's shit.

Willard pours himself a drink from a bottle.

Willard (V.O.)

If that's how Kilgore fought the war . . . I began to wonder what they really had against Kurtz. It wasn't just insanity and murder. There was enough of that to go around for everybody.

EXT. RIVER—FULL SHOT—THE BOAT—DUSK

It is parked, hidden under some trees along the riverbank.

> ### Chef (O.S.)
> I'm not here . . . I'm walking through the jungle gathering mangos, and I meet Raquel Welch. I can make a nice mango cream pudding. You know, kind of spread it around on us . . .

Chef is lying on his back, his eyes closed. Lance is standing on the riverbank next to the PBR. He is taking a leak. He finishes, then turns and squats next to a blue bucket and starts washing his Air-Cav trunks.

> ### Chef (Cont.)
> . . . see, she's into mangoes, too. She's like one limb above me. We're both in the jungle here, nude.

We HEAR a helicopter coming toward the vicinity of the boat. The wind begins to hit the trees and boat.

> ### Clean
> *(to Chief)*
> Hey, Chief? Here comes that colonel guy again.

The SOUND of the helicopter gets closer . . . and an indistinguishable language on a loudspeaker. Lance gathers his bucket and soap and jumps up on the PBR.

> ### Kilgore (Over P.A.)
> "I will not hurt or harm you. Just give me back the board, Lance. It was a good board

and I like it. You know how hard it is to find
a board that you like."

The helicopter drones on into the distance—the same
speech starts again farther off—finally the noise
ceases.

Chef

Determined motherfucker, ain't he? Cock-
sucker!

Willard snaps off a salute at the passing copter.
It disappears into the distance.

Clean

Jesus Christ. That guy's too fucking much,
man.

Lance

Do you think he would've shot us?

Willard

He would've shot us on the beach, or if he
saw me taking his board.

Clean

(singing)
Let's go surfing now, Everybody's learning
how . . .

Lance

Let's get this board out of my turret.

Clean

Sucker.

Lance

Come on, how am I gonna shoot him the next
time he comes around?

Willard
Hey, Chef, make some room back there for the
board.

They stow the board in the back of the boat, hiding
it.

Chief
I wonder if that's the same chopper.

Willard
Hell, he's probably got them all over the
river with that recording. We'll have to
hold up here till dark, Chief.
  (to Lance)
Don't worry, Lance, he won't follow us too far.

Lance
What makes you say that?

Willard
You think that Cav colonel wants everyone up
river to know we stole his board?

Lance
I didn't steal it!

Willard laughs, lights up a cigarette.

Chief
Captain? Just how far up this river are we
going?

Willard
That's classified, Chief. I can't tell you.
We're going up pretty far.

Clean
Is it gonna be hairy?

                              Willard
I don't know, kid. Yeah, probably.

                              Chief
You like it like that, Captain? When it's
hot, hairy?

                              Willard
Fuck.
     (a beat)
Maybe you'll get a chance to know what the
fuck you are in some factory in Ohio.

Chef steps forward with a plastic bucket.

                              Chef
Hey, Chief, I'm gonna go get those mangoes
now, okay?

                              Chief
Take somebody with you.

                              Willard
I'll go with him.

He turns and follows Chef off the PBR. They climb
up the bank, away from the boat, into the jungle.

EXT. JUNGLE—MED. VIEW—DUSK

Chef and Willard cautiously walk through the dark
underbrush. We SEE fragments of them, LOSE them
occasionally, and just MOVE through the jungle. WE
HEAR this conversation throughout:

                              Willard
Chef?

                    Chef
Yes, sir.

                  Willard
How come they call you that?

                    Chef
Call me what, sir?

                  Willard
Chef. 'Cause you like mangoes and stuff?

                    Chef
No, sir. I'm a real chef. I'm a saucier.

                  Willard
Saucier?

                    Chef
Yes, sir. See, I come from New Orleans. I
was raised to be a saucier. A great saucier.

                  Willard
What's a saucier?

                    Chef
We specialize in sauces. Gotta be a mango
tree here somewhere . . . Then, I was supposed
to go to Paris, to the Escoffier School. But
then I got orders for my physical.

As they move deeper into the jungle:

                    Chef
Hell, I joined the navy. Heard they had better food. Cook school, that did it.

                  Willard
Oh, yeah? How's that?

Chef puts down his bucket and rifle, takes a leak. Willard takes a few steps farther in the jungle and then sits by him on a log.

                              Chef
        You don't wanna hear about that. They
        lined us up in front of a hundred yards of
        prime rib. All of us, you know, looking at
        it? Magnificent meat. Really. Beautifully
        marbled. Magnifique. Next thing, they're
        throwing the meat into these big caul-
        drons.

Willard has heard something in the jungle during this explanation. He becomes alert.

                              Chef
        All of it. Boiling it. I looked inside, man,
        it was turning gray. I couldn't fucking
        believe that one! That's when I applied for
        radioman's school, but they—

Chef looks up, seeing Willard standing a distance away, poised with his rifle. Willard signals to him to come cautiously. He motions to Chef to move with him, each covering the other. They walk a few yards from where they have heard something move.

                              Chef
            (whispering)
        What is it? Charlie?

MED. SHOT—PANNING—WILLARD

moving through the jungle cautiously, he is comfortable in this environment. He signals and directs

his way very expertly, giving silent instructions to Chef on how to move with him.

They seem to have the intruder localized and proceed very quietly toward where he is.

MED. SHOT—THE ELEPHANT GRASS—WILLARD AND CHEF

Suddenly the grass folds almost to Willard, and a huge TIGER leaps out at them, snarling magnificently. They fire wildly, emptying their clips.

> **Chef**
> It's a motherfucking tiger! It's a tiger, man! A tiger!

He turns and bolts through the jungle, as scared as a man can be.

> **Chef**
> Motherfucking tiger!

Willard backs out of the clearing, covering the bushes and runs, scared out of his head as well. They fire their M16s indiscriminately, running back to the boat, screaming.

FULL SHOT—THE BOAT

The crew is armed. They've heard the screaming. Lance has the twin fifties pointed into the jungle. Chef comes screaming out of the brush. Throws his rifle in the boat and dives headfirst after it.

Chief

Battle stations. Lance, up front. Get on your sixty, Clean.

Chef

Fucking tiger!

Clean

Let's go!

Chef

Chief, you were right. Never get out of the fucking boat!

Chief

Clean, bring that 60 forward.

Chef

Never get out of the boat! I gotta remember! Gotta remember! Never get out of the boat!

Chief

How many is it?

Chef

A fucking tiger!

Clean

What?

Chef

Tiger!

Chief

Tiger?

Chef

(going berserk)

I'm done with this goddamn fucking shit!
You can kiss my ass on the county square,
because I'm fucking bugging out! I don't
fucking need it! I don't want it! I didn't
get on the goddamn A train for this kind
of shit! All I wanted to do is fucking
cook! I just wanted to learn to fucking
cook, man!

The others try to calm him down.

Lance
You're all right. You're all right.

Chef
All right. It's gonna be all right. It's
gonna be all right. Never get out of the
fucking boat. 'Bye, tiger! 'Bye, tiger!

The boat pulls away as he continues ranting about
the tiger.

CLOSE ON WILLARD

looking back into the jungle.

Willard (V.O.)
Never get out of the boat. Absolutely goddamn right. Unless you were going all the
way.

EXT. RIVER—THE PBR—NIGHT

The PBR moves down the dark, silent river through
the night.

>   **Willard (V.O.)**
> Kurtz got off the boat. He split from the
> whole fucking program. How did that happen?
> What did he see here that first tour?

Willard lights a cigarette and holds a flashlight
as he looks at the dossier. As he speaks we see
CLOSE SHOTS on the newspaper articles, letters,
and photos.

>   **Willard (V.O.)**
> Thirty-eight fucking years old. If you
> joined the Green Berets, there was no way
> you'd ever get above colonel. Kurtz knew
> what he was giving up. The more I read and
> began to understand, the more I admired
> him. His family and friends couldn't under-
> stand it. And they couldn't talk him out of
> it. He had to apply three times, and he put
> up with a ton of shit, but when he threat-
> ened to resign, they gave it to him. The
> next youngest guy in his class was half his
> age. They must've thought he was some far-
> out old man humping it over that course.
> I did it when I was nineteen, it damn
> near wasted me. A tough motherfucker. He
> finished it.

>   **Willard (V.O.)**
> He could've gone for general, but he went
> for himself, instead.

MEDIUM VIEW OF THE PBR

gliding up the river. Chef is sitting in the back
of the boat, writing a letter. He is using a flash-

light to see by, and he reads to himself outloud as
he writes.

> **Chef**
> *(writing letter)*
> Dear Eva. Today was really a new one. Almost
> got eaten alive by a fucking tiger. Really
> un-fucking believable, you know? We're tak-
> ing this guy, Captain Willard, up the river,
> but he hasn't told us yet where we're taking
> him . . .

Clean is at the helm, singing to himself, the Chief
is sleeping. Willard looks at an article about Kurtz
in a magazine.

> **Willard (V.O.)**
> October, 1967. On special assignment, Kon-
> toom Province, Two-Corps . . . Kurtz staged
> Operation Archangel with combined local
> forces. Rated a major success. He received
> no official clearance. He just thought it up
> and did it. What balls. They were going to
> nail his ass to the floorboards for that
> one. But after the press got a hold of it,
> they promoted him to full colonel instead.
> Oh, man, the bullshit piled up so fast in
> Vietnam, you needed wings to stay above it.

Suddenly, from around a bend, the boat is illuminated by a strange artificial light. Lance and Chief
are awakened. Willard reacts as he looks out toward
the light. It becomes brighter and brighter as they
move closer.

WHAT THEY SEE:

EXT. HAU PHAT—FULL VIEW—NIGHT

The PBR goes by the base, tents, oil drums, sand-bagged bunkers, etc., but the biggest surprise of all is a huge oval STAGE built in the water, lit by banks of lights. Preparations for some sort of show are in progress.

They all react, incredulous, as the PBR pulls into the bay and up to the dock.

> Clean
>
> This sure enough is a bizarre sight in the middle of all this shit.

> Chief
>
> *(to Willard)*
> Expecting us this time?

> Willard
>
> Damned if I know.

It looks like an amusement park, with strings of lights, etc.

> Chef
>
> Jesus Christ . . .

EXT. SUPPLY DOCK AREA—NIGHT

The supply docks of this base. Tents, oil drums, sandbagged bunkers, helicopters, tanks, guns, and men. As they walk, Chef and Clean stop a moment and look at a group of motorcycles. The dock is crowded with all kinds of goods, freezers, refrigerators, etc., all the nonessentials for fighting a war.

> Clean
>
> Hau Phat. You ever been up here before, Chef?

                              Chef
I bet you could score up here.

                              Clean
Yo, man, check out the bikes, man. Yamaha,
Suzuki.

                              Chef
That's a good one.

                              Clean
Yeah, Sukiyaki.

Willard moves on, Chef and Clean catch up with him.

                              Clean
This must be the guy.

                             Willard
Right over there.

Willard and the men approach a harried SERGEANT at
a requisition desk, filling out papers, answering
questions, shouting out orders to the frenetic
activity around him. There are soldiers scurrying
back and forth, loading and unloading supplies.
They constantly interrupt the sergeant with their
questions.

Chef and Clean stop in front of the sergeant.

                              Clean
Three drums of diesel fuel, PBR-Five...

The sergeant reacts, still bothered by constant
interruptions from the soldiers around him.

                            Sergeant
Move! We have one hour, that's all!

                               72

(to Clean)
What do you want?

Chef
Can I get some Panana Rod?

Sergeant
Panama Red? Yeah, I'll get you Panama Red.

Clean
Sergeant.

Sergeant
Destination?

Clean
I don't have a destination.

Sergeant
You can't get a goddamn thing without a destination.

Willard steps in.

Willard
Sergeant.

Sergeant
I need a destination. I can't do a goddamn thing about it.

Willard
Hey, Sarge, these guys are with me. Destination's classified. I carry priority papers from Com-Sec Intelligence, II Corps.

Sergeant
Listen, sir, it's a real big night—

(to another soldier)
Eight dollars for that camera—

With unexpected rage, Willard suddenly reaches up
and grabs the Sergeant by the collar, pulling him
down across a table, really frightening him. Everybody is quite surprised.

Willard
Just give them some fuel.

Sergeant
You got it.

Willard lets go of the sergeant, almost embarrassed
for the show of temper. The sergeant goes back
behind his desk and starts signing the papers.

Sergeant
Listen, Captain . . . I'm really sorry about
tonight. It's really bad around here. Just
take this over to the man at the supply desk
and you got it.

He tears off the requisition and hands it to one of
the trio.

Sergeant
(to crew)
Listen, would you guys like some press box
seats for the show? You want those? The
show, man, out here. The bunnies.

Lance
The Playboy bunnies?

The sergeant finally leaves the trio, grabs a bottle
of cognac, and moves to Willard. Hands him the bottle.

Sergeant
Hey, listen, Captain . . . on the house. No
hard feelings.

Willard looks down at the bottle in his hand and
then up at the stage.

DISSOLVE TO:

The SOUND of ENGINES is heard. A HUEY and TWO LOCHES
descend from the clouds. The Loches hover and cir-
cle, while the Huey descends onto the platform
stage. There is a large black-and-white PLAYBOY
INSIGNIA painted on the nose.

EXT. STAGE—FULL SHOT—NIGHT

The entire arena around the stage and right up to
the barbed wire is mobbed with hundreds of
seething American fighting men. Some of these boys
have just gotten here, others have been in the
jungle for months. It's the Vietnam military version of a happening. Guys from all walks of life,
from all cities, guys with flowers in their hair
and peace signs around their necks, other guys
with their short-time sticks and war medallions
around their necks. Black G.I.s congregate
together with their clenched-fist black power
medallions. There are signs and posters and graf-
fiti everywhere. Some guys have guitars, everyone
seems to have a camera. Rummaging, sitting, waiting expectantly, before the enormous stage, which
is protected by rings of concertina wire, a moat,
and MPs every three feet at riot control positions. Many joints and pipes are being passed
around. Snapshots are being taken. It has a strong

resemblance to a love-in or even Woodstock. Except that they're all in various degrees of combat fatigues, and they're all men.

CHEF, CLEAN, LANCE, WILLARD, AND THE CHIEF move down an aisle to their seats. It is through WILLARD'S EYES that we see this spectacle, and every so often we will see an enthusiastic Lance, Chef, and Clean. The Chief remains noncommittal, and somewhat bored. To the others it's a wonder of wonders.

Over by the dock, behind a chain-link fence, there is a group of VIETNAMESE who have gathered to watch the show. They have brought rice, food, etc. They will watch and react throughout, along with the American soldiers who are standing guard in front of them.

VIEW ON THE STAGE

The Playboy copter descends onto the stage. The door of the Huey slides open and TWO YOUNG GREEN BERETS step out with their M16s to varied CATCALLS. When this abates, a young, extremely well-dressed man emerges. He is the epitome of the Hollywood agent. He's informal, high-strung, and good at what he does. His presence causes some stirring and occasional shouts of "ripoff" from the men. He gets a microphone from the stage, then walks to the front and addresses the men.

> **Agent**
> How you doing out there?
> *(beat and reaction)*
> I said how you doing out there?
> *(beat and reaction)*
> Wanna say hello to you from all of us up
> here, to all of you out there, who work so

goddamn hard on Operation Brute Force.
Hello, all you paratroopers out there! And
the Marines! And the sailors! We wanna let
you know that we're proud of you, 'cause we
know how tough and how hard it's been! Yeah!
And to prove it, we're gonna give you some
entertainment we know you're gonna like!

The band starts its rock 'n' roll amp, playing the
Creedence Clearwater Revival rendition of "Suzy Q."

                    Agent
    Miss August, Miss Sandra Beatty! Miss May,
    Miss Terri Teray! And the Playmate of the
    Year, Miss Carrie Foster!

Two very beautiful PLAYMATES in exotic, brief cos-
tumes come out of the helicopter. They are TERRI
and SANDRA, and they start swaying to the music.

                   Sandra
    Hello out there!

The two Playmates jump down and dance to the front
of the stage. The G.I.s go crazy as the girls dance
their erotic dance. In the meantime, the two Green
Berets at the helicopter help out the PLAYMATE OF
THE YEAR, CARRIE FOSTER.

The Berets carry the Playmate out on their rifles to
the center of the stage, and put her down. She
dances forward and joins the other two girls at the
front. Carrie is dressed in a Western outfit. They
all dance to "Suzy Q."

VIEW ON THE CROWD

Appropriately, they go wild.

> **Marine**
> I'm coming, honey!

MONTAGE ON THE GIRLS

Various shots as they dance their erotic dance.

CLOSER ANGLE ON WILLARD AND THE PBR CREW

sitting in the press box, watching the whole spectacle. Then Chef, Lance, and Clean rise from their seats and wander into the crowd of G.I.s, enjoying the show.

MONTAGE ON THE MEN

Some of the guys are dancing with each other, some are clapping their hands, some are cheering, other continue to smoke dope. It is a happening.

ANGLE ON THE PLAYMATES

Sandra and Terri turn and cross to the two Green Berets. They take their M16s, and go through a routine as the men go crazy.

> **Marine**
> Grease my gun!

Chef and Lance are in the part of the audience that is in front of Terri.

> **Terri**
> *(to Chef)*
> You're cute. I like you.

                              Chef
          I'm here, baby! I'm here!

                              Lance
              (to Terri)
          You fucking bitch!

MED. CLOSE SHOT—THE AGENT

looking a little worried.

ANGLE ON WILLARD AND THE CHIEF

watching the spectacle. Willard takes a drink from
the bottle that was given to him by the supply sergeant.

HIS POV

The three Playmates going through all their gyra-
tions.

MED. CLOSE SHOT—WILLARD

Reacting, shaking his head. Chef, Lance, and Clean
all think it's fantastic.

VIEW ON THE CROWD

Audience continues to react as the three Playmates
sway and hump. Fights are breaking out. Some of the
G.I.s pull out centerfolds of the three girls from
under their uniforms.

Marine
Sign my centerfold!

He leaps madly, climbing up on the stage. Other guys start to follow him. The MPs try to stop them to no avail. Before you know it, a mob is storming the stage.

VIEW ON AGENT

Knows the show is over.

Agent
(to pilot)
Start her up.
(to MPs)
Get the girls! Let's go!
(to crowd)
So long!

The Playmates are helped back into the helicopter. The rotors whine and the Huey lifts off just as the first of the enthusiastic mob reaches it. The agent sets off a smoke bomb to disperse the crowd. Some guys are even hanging onto the skids of the helicopter. They finally let go and fall into the water below, as the helicopter flies away.

Willard (V.O.)
Charlie didn't get much U.S.O. He was dug in too deep or moving too fast. His idea of great R and R was cold rice, and a little rat meat. He had only two ways home—death, or victory.

EXT. HAU PHAT—DAY

As the PBR pulls away from the Hau Phat area, Willard looks back at the clean-up operations, a helicopter hovers over the littered area, shirtless men sweep and mop up the stage, burn trash; other dismantle the floating lights.

> **Willard (V.O.)**
> No wonder Kurtz put a weed up Command's ass. The war was being run by a bunch of four-star clowns, who were gonna end up giving the whole circus away.

EXT. PBR—DAY

Chief is steering the boat. Chef is looking at a *Playboy* magazine centerfold of Terri.

> **Chef**
> You know, man, that was far fucking out. I collected every picture of her since she was Miss December.
> *(showing Clean the centerfold)*
> Hey, Clean, look at that. She was here, man! I even wrote to the cunt. She didn't write me back.

> **Clean**
> You can get really hung up on these broads, like that cat in the delta.

> **Chef**
> Yeah. What cat?

As Clean talks, Chef tears the centerfold out of his *Playboy*, then kneels down by the bulkhead in back of the wheel. He tapes the centerfold onto the bulkhead.

> **Clean**
> The one that went up for murder? He was an army Sergeant. This cat, he really dug his *Playboy*, man.

As he continues, Lance moves to the back of the boat and starts unwrapping the plastic from his new water skis.

> **Clean**
> I mean, this cat, when the thing arrived, he was there to meet it, man!

> **Chef**
> *(indicating photo)*
> Look at these beautiful fucking jugs, man!

> **Clean**
> Anyway, he was working ARVN patrols, had one of them cocky gook asshole lieutenants, and one day the gook took his magazine and wouldn't give it back! Cat said, "Gimme my magazine back!" Gook said, "You shut up. I have you court-martialed," you know?

> **Chef**
> Typical fucking ARVN, man.

> **Clean**
> The gook went too far.

> **Chief**
> Chef, take the wheel.

Chef takes the wheel of the boat as Chief moves back and starts brushing his teeth. Lance continues to unwrap his skis.

Clean
Sticking pinholes and mutilating the centerfold and shit like that.

Clean
And the sergeant said, "You better not do that to her. You leave your shitty little gook hands off of that girl!" Gook say, "Fuck you!" in Vietnamese, right? Sergeant, man, he just couldn't handle it no more. He just picked up his iron—

He picks up an M16 rifle to demonstrate.

Clean
—flipped it to rock 'n' roll and boom! Gave that little zero a long burst straight through the *Playboy* mag. It blew his ass clear off the dock. There wasn't no more lieutenant that day. That was it for his ass.

Chief
They burn him for it?

Clean
The sergeant? Yeah, man. They stuck his ass in the LBJ. It's too bad he didn't get no medals or nothing.

He puts the rifle back in the rack. Disappears down into the hole of the ship. They all shake their heads at the cruel injustice of life.

Chef
Fucking ARVN, man. They should've killed

the fuck. Should've given that fucker a
Silver Star. Bummer for the gook, though,
ain't it?

EXT. RIVER—THE PBR—DAY

We HEAR a radio station playing. Willard is seated,
looking through the dossier, documents from the CIA.

> **Radio Host (Over Radio)**
> Good morning, Vietnam. I'm Army Specialist
> Zack Johnson on AMVN. It's about eighty-two
> degrees in downtown Saigon right now, also
> very humid...

Clean is standing on the front of the boat, he has
a small transistor radio in his hand.

> **Radio Host (Over Radio)**
> ...and we have an important message for
> all GI's who are living offbase from the
> mayor of Saigon. He'd like you to hang the
> laundry up indoors, instead of on the win-
> dowsills. The mayor wants you to keep
> Saigon beautiful. And now, here's another
> blast from the past going out to Big Sam,
> who's all alone out there with the First
> Battalion, 35th Infantry, and dedicated by
> the Fire Team and their groovy C.O. The
> Rolling Stones, "Satisfaction."

The MUSIC comes on, Clean starts dancing, keeping
time to "Satisfaction." The others cheer him.

> **Chef**
> Work out, Clean! Get down, bubba!
> *(to Lance)*
> Hang on, Lance!

We SEE that Lance is water-skiing behind the PBR, waving to the guys.

                        Clean
        (dancing)
        Can you dig it, man? Can you dig it?
        (to Chef)
        I see you're right on target.
        (to group)
        Work out! Yeah! Yeah!

The boat passes a Vietnamese fishing boat, capsizing it in its wake.

VIEW ON WILLARD

He's found himself in a corner in the boat. He looks to the front where Clean is moving and dancing to the MUSIC, to the rear where Lance is water-skiing, and looks down to his dossier, with its odd assortment of photographs, reports, and letters.

                    Willard (V.O.)
        "Commitment and Counterinsurgency" by
        Walter E. Kurtz. "As long as our officers
        and troops perform tours of duty limited to
        one year, they will remain dilettantes in
        war, and tourists in Vietnam. As long as
        cold beer, hot food, rock 'n' roll, and all
        the other amenities remain expected norm,
        our conduct of the war will gain only impo-
        tence. We need fewer men, and better. If
        they were committed, this war could be won
        with a fourth of our present force."

FULL SHOT—THE PBR CREW—DAY

The Chief is at the helm. He takes off his sun-
glasses and looks straight ahead, reacting.

HIS POV:

TWO PBR's coming straight at them. The lead PBR is
headed on a collision course.

                    Clean
     Shit. Chicken time. You ain't shittin', bro.
     They're motherfuckers.

                    Lance
     Who is that? What's going on?

All are looking forward. The Chief grabs a loud-hailer.

                    Chief
          (over loud-hailer)
     Is that you, Lazzaro?

                    Chef
          (to Chief)
     Don't chicken out.

The lead PBR keeps coming on in a game of
"chicken," the rock music blaring from its speakers. Then it swerves at the last possible moment
and fishtails past. One if its CREWMEN moons our
crew. Lance, Chef, and Clean shout back and give
them the finger.

                  Loudspeaker
     Chicken!

The other PBR fishtails past also, causing a lot of
turbulence in the water. The crew gives our boys

the finger, then one of them throws a SMOKE BOMB. It lands on the canopy.

The smoke bomb spews out its YELLOW SMOKE, and suddenly the canopy catches on fire.

>   Chief
>   Fire on the canopy!

Chef grabs a fire extinguisher and tries to snuff the fire out.

>   Chef
>   I got it! Get out of there!

Chief keeps roaring down the river as the others continue to fight the fire. Finally they get it put out. Willard stands there, dumbfounded, and reacting, as we:

                                        DISSOLVE TO:

EXT. RIVER—THE PBR—DAY

The PBR continues down the river. Lance gives a handful of palm leaves to Chef, who is sitting up on top of the canvas roof, trying to patch up the hole that was caused by the fire. Clean has a pair of drumsticks and is beating out a drum rhythm, really getting into it.

Willard studies the dossier; some photos and Vietnamese I.D. cards.

>   Willard (V.O.)
>   Late summer, autumn 1968. Kurtz's patrol
>   in the highlands is coming under frequent
>   bush. The camp started falling apart.

November. Kurtz orders assassination of three Vietnamese men and one woman. Two of the men were colonels in the South Vietnamese Army. Enemy activity in his old sector dropped off to nothing. Guess he must have hit the right four people.

IMAGE OF THE GENERAL

> **General to Willard (V.O.)**
> He joined the Special Forces, and after that he . . .

BACK TO WILLARD

> **Willard (V.O.)**
> The army tried one last time to bring him back into the fold. And if he'd pulled over, it all would have been forgotten.

> **General to Willard (V.O.)**
> . . . unsound.

> **Willard (V.O.)**
> But he kept going. And he kept winning it his way.

> **Colonel to Willard (V.O.)**
> . . . with this Montagnard army of his.

> **Willard (V.O.)**
> And they called me in.

> **Colonel to Willard (V.O.)**
> . . . like a god, and follow every order, however ridiculous.

                    Willard (V.O.)
They lost him. He was gone. Nothing but
rumors and random intelligence, mostly from
captured V.C. The V.C. knew his name by now,
and they were scared of him.

                    Willard (V.O.)
He and his men were playing hit and run all
the way into Cambodia.

Clean's drum rhythm is annoying Willard. He puts a
map back into his dossier, rises, and looks at Clean,
pissed, then looks to the Chief.

                        Chief
Clean.

Clean stops drumming, moves away.

                       Willard
    (to Chief)
How long has that kid been on this boat?

                        Chief
Seven months.

                       Willard
He's really specializing in busting my balls.

                        Chief
Very possibly, Captain, he thinks the same
of you.

Willard moves over to Chief.

                       Willard
Oh, yeah? What do you think, Chief?

ANGLE ON CLEAN

Clean gives Willard the finger behind his back.

Chief
I don't think. My orders say I'm not supposed to know where I'm taking this boat, so
I don't. But one look at you and I know it's
gonna be hot, wherever it is.

Willard comes into the cabin, looks at the Chief.

Willard
We're going up river, about seventy-five
clicks above the Do Lung bridge.

The Chief reacts, figuring it out almost immediately.

Chief
That's Cambodia, Captain.

Willard
That's classified. We're not supposed to be
in Cambodia, but that's where I'm going. You
just get me close to my destination, and
I'll cut you and the crew loose.

Chief
All right, Captain.

DISSOLVE TO:

EXT. THE RIVER PBR—DAY

The PBR moves down the river. Willard is studying
the dossier, holding a LETTER from Kurtz to his son.

Willard (V.O.)
"Dear Son. I'm afraid that both you and your

mother will have been worried at not hearing from me during the past weeks, but my
situation here has become a difficult one. I
have been officially accused of murder by
the army. The alleged victims were four
Vietnamese double agents. We spent months
uncovering them and accumulating evidence.
When absolute proof was completed, we acted.
We acted like soldiers. The charges are
unjustified. "They are, in fact, and under
the circumstances of this conflict, quite
completely insane."

The boat moves past some DEAD AMERICAN PILOTS.
Their bodies are lying in the water, on the bank,
and in trees, all torn apart and bloody. There is
smoke and debris all around.

Willard (V.O.)
In a war, there are many moments for com-
passion and tender action. There are many
moments for ruthless action. What is often
called ruthless, but may, in many circumstances, be only clarity. Seeing clearly
what there is to be done, and doing it
directly, quickly, awake.

They come upon a burning helicopter, which has
crashed in one of the trees on the shore. This
explains the dead American bodies. The Chief picks
up the radio phone, calling into headquarters.

Chef (Into Radio)
Request dust-off. Three, maybe four KIAs.

Willard (V.O.)
"I will trust you to tell your mother what
you choose about this letter. As for the

charges against me, I am unconcerned. I am beyond their timid, lying morality, and so I am beyond caring. You have all my faith. Your loving father."

CLOSE ON A SHADOWY PHOTO OF KURTZ

The caption "Photo believed to be Col. W. E. Kurtz."

DISSOLVE TO:

EXT. RIVER OUTPOST—DAY

It is a tremendous, tropical rainfall. The PBR pulls in toward an American outpost that is being used as a forward medical evacuation center. Various helicopter pads are seen but only one helicopter—the one painted with the Playboy bunny logo that brought the girls to Hau Phat. The whole area is a mess with mud and debris and looks deserted.

> **Willard**
> *(reacting)*
> Jesus.

> **Chief**
> No wonder I couldn't get them on the radio.

> **Willard**
> What a dump.

Several soldiers in raincoats come out from a tent as the PBR pulls up.

> **Soldier**
> Hi there!

Willard

How you doing?

Soldier

That's a nice little boat you got there.
Never seen one up here before.

Chief

We called in a request for a medevac. You
guys didn't receive it?

Soldier

Medevac? No.

Chief

We passed a downed Huey with some KIAs.

Soldier

On your way here?

Chief

Yeah.

Soldier
(incredulous)
You're going up this river?

Chief

Way up.

Soldier

Way up river? Forget it.

Chief

Why?

Soldier

We wanna send some people down river. Just
forget it.

They turn around and start to go back to their tent.

> **Chef**
> *(to Willard)*
> What the fuck was that?

> **Chief**
> *(calling out)*
> We'll be back in a couple of days.

The soldier looks at him as though he must be crazy.

> **Soldier**
> Yeah, right, you'll be back.

They return to the tent. Willard steps off the PBR.

> **Willard**
> Chief?

> **Chief**
> Yeah, Captain.

> **Willard**
> See what you can do with that engine. I'm gonna have a look around. And don't leave without me.

He walks up the muddy bank and through the deserted camp. Half of it is blown down. The whole installation has the look of a ghost town. TWO SOLDIERS approach, huddled in their ponchos.

> **Willard**
> Hey, soldier, where's your C.O.?

> **Soldier**
> Don't ask me, man.

Willard wanders around the desolate place. Other soldiers pass.

> **Willard**
> Hey, guys, where's your C.O.?

> **Soldier**
> He stepped on a land mine about two months ago. Got all blowed to hell.

> **Willard**
> Who's in charge here?

> **Soldier**
> Charge? I don't know, man. I'm just the night man. Just doing what I'm told. I'm just a working girl.

He just giggles and turns off walking into the mud and rain.

> **Willard**
> *(to other soldier)*
> What about you, fella?

The other soldier turns around smiling idiotically, and making animal noises. He stumbles off after his friend.

EXT. PBR—BY THE RIVER

Lance, Chef, and Clean are sitting on the dock surrounded by an enormous pile of clothes, boots, all sorts of brand new junk, seemingly abandoned. Chief remains with the boat. Clean is working on Lance's M16.

Lance, man, I'm telling you it's gonna jam.
You mark my words.

Lance

Get off my back!

Lance, in an unexplainable fit of temper, turns to
Clean, jumping on him and pulling him into the mud.
Chef, seeing a brawl, jumps into it as well. All
wrestle in the mud.

BACK TO WILLARD

— He hears a voice.

Agent

Hey, you! Come here!

Willard turns to see the Hollywood agent from the
Hau Phat show under the flap of a large tent, hiding
from the rain, waving Willard to come over.

His clothes are the same ones he wore at the Hau
Phat show but wet and dirty. He motions Willard
over to him.

Agent

Come here. Is that your boat? Come on
inside.

Willard

What do you want?

Agent

Come on inside, I want to talk to you. Come
on. Get out of the rain.

BACK TO THE CREW IN THE MUD

Rolling around, berserkly fighting, slapping mud on each other. It's as though there is a lingering madness that infects anyone who visits this place.

> **Chief**
> Come on, cut the shit. Come on.

BACK TO WILLARD AND THE AGENT

> **Agent**
> How you doing, Captain? I want you to meet some people.

CUT TO:

THE CREW AT THE PBR, STILL FIGHTING IN THE MUD

Willard approaches the group. He looks down at them as they sprawl around in the mud.

> **Willard**
> Hey, guys. Hey, fellas. Guys?

They don't respond, but continue their wild free-for-all in the junk and mud.

> **Willard**
> I just made a deal with the people from Hau Phat. I negotiated two barrels of fuel for a couple of hours with the bunnies.

They stop fighting instantly. Willard walks toward the boat. The group of them run after him.

                    Chef
You shittin' me?

                   Willard
No, I'm not.
    (to crew)
Grab a couple of barrels and get up to that
big tent. Come on!

VIEW ON THE CHIEF

He is not as jubilant about this news.

                   Chief
Captain. You're giving away our fuel for a
Playmate of the Month?

                   Willard
No. Playmate of the Year, Chief.
    *(he takes a drink from a
    bottle)*

                   Chief
Captain, we get in a fire fight and run out
of fuel, I want you to tell me how she
was.

                   Willard
I made a deal for all of us, Chief. How about
you?

                   Chief
You got some mamas in there?

                   Willard
Some what?

                    Chief
          (laughing)
    Forget it, Captain. I'll stay with the boat.

Chief moves to the engine, with Lance's M16.

                    Lance
    Hey, Captain, give me a hand!

Willard helps Lance with the fuel drum, and they
exit, leaving Chief alone on the boat.

EXT. PLAYBOY HELICOPTER—RAIN

It is still raining. The PLAYBOY HELICOPTER
is parked by the river. OUR VIEW MOVES CLOSER, and
we can make out two figures sitting in the front
seat.

                    Chef (O.S.)
    You know, I got every one of your pic-
    tures . . .

INT. PLAYBOY HELICOPTER—RAIN

It is Chef and Terri. He has on his rain gear and
is struggling to get it off. Terri is holding a
white BIRD in her hands and there are TWO MORE
perched on their seat backs.

                    Chef
    I got the centerfold, the Playmate's Review,
    the Playmate of the Year runoff. I even got
    the calendar. Hey, oiseau! How come you got
    a bird?

                              Terri
I used to be the bird girl at Busch Gardens.

                              Chef
Busch Gardens?

                              Terri
Yeah, I used to train birds there.

He reacts as he rises, struggling to get off his
rain pants.

                              Chef
You are Miss December, aren't you?

                              Terri
Miss May.

INT. HOSPITAL UNIT—RAIN

Lance and Carrie are inside one of the hospital
musk units. She is lying back on one of the beds,
and Lance is trying to pull her boot off. Carrie's
portfolios and pictures are spread around the bed
with some of her fan mail.

                              Carrie
Is it coming?

BACK TO CHEF AND TERRI

                              Chef
Miss December has black hair.

                              Terri
It's over there.

She points to the backseat of the Huey, to a black
wig on a stand. Chef reacts as he looks at it. She
is still preoccupied with the bird.

> **Terri**
> He's not one of my regular birds.
> *(to bird)*
> Come on, baby. Snatch your cracker. Come
> here.

BACK TO LANCE AND CARRIE

Lance is kneeling next to Carrie, starting to make
his move. He opens her blouse, exposing her
breasts.

> **Carrie**
> Being Playmate of the Year is the loneliest
> experience I can imagine. It's like you try
> to express your feelings to someone, and
> show them your heart . . .

BACK TO CHEF AND TERRI

> **Chef**
> Yeah, I'd love to see your bird act, but
> would you mind just putting this—would you
> just mind putting this black wig on for me,
> please?

He picks up the wig from the stand. Terri turns and
moves back to the rear seat.

BACK TO LANCE AND CARRIE

He moves to her makeup case.

> ### Carrie
> ...and there's this glass wall between
> you, this invisible glass, and they can see
> your mouth moving.

BACK TO CHEF AND TERRI

She is seated next to him in the backseat of the
helicopter. He puts the black wig on her.

> ### Terri
> I used to train birds for at least two years
> at Busch Gardens.

> ### Chef
> This was cascading over your shoulder.
> *(her blouse)*
> This was open here.

BACK TO LANCE AND CARRIE

Lance is putting barrettes in her hair.

> ### Carrie
> ...but they can't hear what you're saying.

BACK TO TERRI AND CHEF

He has opened her blouse and is trying to position
her.

> ### Terri
> ...I used to train them to stand on their
> head, fly upside down, and ride little bicy-
> cles...

                              Chef
          Your right hand was over there . . .

Suddenly Clean appears at the back window of the
helicopter, carrying an open black umbrella to
shield himself from the rain. He bangs on the
window.

                             Clean
            Hey, Chef!

                              Chef
            Get out of here, man!

Clean continues to pound on the side of the helicopter. Chef reacts on the inside.

                              Chef
            Later! Later! Give me fifteen minutes.

BACK TO LANCE AND CARRIE

Lance puts some of the green makeup on Carrie.

                            Carrie
            You can never really make them hear what
            you're trying to say...

BACK TO CHEF AND TERRI

Trying to position her.

                              Chef
            You were kind of bending. Yeah, your ass was
            just kind of . . .

By this time Clean has climbed up on the roof of the helicopter, he leans over and looks in at Chef and Terri through the front window, banging on it with his umbrella.

> **Chef**
> Hey man, fuck off! Fifteen minutes!

BACK TO LANCE AND CARRIE

He is lying her back on the bed.

> **Carrie**
> That's why I tried so desperately to show somebody that I had some talent.

BACK TO CHEF AND TERRI

Chef fixes her shirt.

> **Terri**
> Little baby Macaws. Have you ever seen a baby Macaw? They're beautiful.

Clean is now looking in through the window of the door. They react to him.

> **Chef**
> (to Clean)
> Come on, man, take off!

> **Clean**
> I got my rights, man!

BACK TO LANCE AND CARRIE

He puts more makeup on her, as she continues to talk.

                    Carrie
     They make you do things that you don't want
     to do. Like this picture here.

She opens the portfolio that she has been hanging
on to. We SEE a picture of her in the nude. Lance
looks at it and reacts. Then she resumes talking.

                    Carrie
     I started feeling repulsed with myself . . .

BACK TO CHEF AND TERRI

                    Chef
     You were just kind of bending forward, your
     ass kind of out.

                    Terri
     I love training birds . . .

                    Chef
     That's it.

                    Terri
     . . . I really do.

Chef finally has her posed perfectly.

                    Chef
     That's it! Voilà! Beautiful.

We realize that he was trying to get her to pose
exactly as she was in the centerfold of the
Playmate of the Year that he taped up on the PBR.

Chef
You know, I can't believe it. Me, J. Hicks.
I can't believe I'm really here, you know?

BACK TO LANCE AND CARRIE

He is caressing her face.

Carrie
. . . Maybe I'm unfit to have a relationship
with a beautiful, innocent boy.

BACK TO CHEF AND TERRI

Chef
Just think, if it hadn't been for the
Vietnam War, I never would've met you, Miss
December.

Terri
Miss May.

BACK TO LANCE AND CARRIE

Carrie
I wish I could find just one person that
could share my point of view.

BACK TO CHEF AND TERRI

They look at each other for a beat, then they both
come unglued. He starts stripping the clothes off
her, laying her back on the seat, kissing her
breasts, etc.

                    Terri
You kiss like a bird! Oh, God! Kiss me!

                    Chef
I love birds!

BACK TO LANCE AND CARRIE

Clean appears at a window. He looks in at them.
Carrie turns and sees him, she jumps from the bed,
panicked, and moves over by a couple of metal COF-
FIN containers. Clean bursts into the room as
Carrie knocks one of the coffins over. The lid pops
open, revealing a NAKED DEAD SOLDIER inside, full
of bullet holes. Carrie screams.

BACK TO CHEF AND TERRI

Making passionate, enthusiastic love.

                    Terri
Like a bird! Take me like a bird! Fly baby!
What are you doing?

                    Chef
I can fly like an eagle!

                    Terri
Like an eagle, baby! Cock it to me! Oh, you
drive me crazy!

BACK TO CARRIE, LANCE AND CLEAN

Clean is gone. Lance is sitting next to Carrie,
comforting her. She is still distraught over seeing
the dead body.

                              Carrie
Lance, that was somebody's son . . . Lance,
there were things that they made me do, that
I didn't want to do. But they said, "Pull
the ribbons between your legs," and I didn't
want to do it. But they said that was what
was expected of me, that that's what people
wanted to see.

Lance reacts, then kisses her. He starts taking off
her blouse. Clean appears at the broken window
behind them. He sticks his head in and looks down
at them, watching, waiting for his turn. Carrie
breaks the embrace and looks up at Clean.

                              Carrie
Who are you?

                              Clean
I'm next, ma'am.

Carrie reacts as we—

                                              CUT TO:

EXT. RIVER—PBR—DAY

The crew are all on the PBR. Clean is at the back
attempting to shave. Chef is sitting in back busy
cooking up one of his specialties on top of the
engine, giving Clean a hard time about the girls.
The Chief is at the helm, a little sore at what's
happening to his crew.

                              Chef
          (to Clean)
Hell, I didn't know you never got no pussy!

                    Clean

Shut the fuck up!

                    Chef

Sure sorry about that. If I had know, I
would have taken you to New Orleans. Teach
you some of the moves.

                    Chief

Lay off, Chef!

Willard studies the shadowy photo of Kurtz we
saw earlier, as Chef teases Clean in the background.

                    Chef

Cherry boy, cherry boy.

                    Clean

You're fucking dumb!

                    Chef

We'll go to New Orleans. I'll get you fixed
up, you prick.

                    Chief

Lay off, Chef.

                    Clean

You're the only prick I see around here. If
I wanna play with a prick, I'll play with my
own.

                    Chef

You wouldn't know what to do with it!

VIEW ON LANCE

Ignoring all this. He is painting his face with brown and green camouflage greasepaint. It is quite ornate—almost psychedelic. He holds a compact in his hand.

                    Chief
Chef, I said lay off! Knock it off! Give him a break! What do you think I said? And give your jaws a rest. And this ain't the army! You are a sailor. So get out of that frizzly army-looking shirt and stop smoking that dope, you hear me?

He looks back to Lance.

                    Chief
Lance, what's with all the green paint?

                    Lance
Camouflage.

                    Chief
How's that?

                    Lance
So they can't see you. They're everywhere, Chief.

The Chief reacts . . . what the hell can he say.

                    Chief
Uh-huh. I want you to stay awake up there, man. You got a job to do.

                                        DISSOLVE TO:

EXT. THE PBR—DAY

The Chief steers the PBR up river and around a
bend. He sees something ahead, shouts to the crew.

                    Chief
        Sampan off the port bow. Sampan off the port
        bow. Let's take a look.

POV VIEW

A SAMPAN, heading down-river, riding low in the water.

                              BACK TO PBR CREW

Everybody on the crew has reacted, as the Chief
continues to bark out orders.

                    Chief
        Lance, bring them in. Clean, on the 60.
        Chef, get a 16. Clean, get on that 60!

Lance jumps up from his hammock, grabs his M16.
Clean shuts off his radio, jumps up and moves to
the M60 machine gun.

By this time Willard has moved up next to the
Chief, wondering what the hell is going on.

                    Willard
        What's up, Chief?

                    Chief
        A junk boat, Captain. We're gonna take a
        routine check.

                    Willard
        Let's forget routine now, and let them go.

                        111

Chief

These boats are running supplies in this delta, Captain. I'm gonna take a look.

Willard

Chief, my mission's got priority here. Hell, you wouldn't even be in this part of the river, it wasn't for me.

Chief

Until we reach your destination, Captain, you're just on for the ride.

Willard realizes that this is a ploy by the Chief to establish his authority. Nothing is going to stop him.

ANOTHER ANGLE—TO INCLUDE SAMPAN AND PBR

The PBR slides alongside the sampan. THREE NERVOUS VIETNAMESE MEN and ONE YOUNG WOMAN look up from baskets of rice, mangoes, fish, etc.

Chief

All right, come on, let's bring it over. Look in that forward hooch. Bring the people out of there.

By this time the third man has crossed forward and joined the others.

Chef

Hurry up, motherfucker! Move it! *Can couc!*

They hand their ID cards to Chef.

Chief

Keep your eyes open, Clean.

> **Clean**
> *(on the machine gun)*
> I got you, Chief.

Willard just sits down, resigned to this show of the Chief's authority.

Chef looks at them and nods his approval. He hands them to the Chief.

> **Chef**
> That's them. They're okay.

The Chief looks at the ID cards and boat registration, then casually remarks to Chef.

> **Chief**
> Board it and search it.

> **Chef**
> There ain't nothing on it, Chief.

> **Chief**
> Board it and search it.

> **Chef**
> Just baskets and ducks. Bananas. There ain't nothing on it.

> **Chief**
> Go on it and search it.

> **Chef**
> Just a goat. Some fish. Bunch of fucking vegetables.

The Chief finally gets pissed off, he turns and screams at Chef:

                              Chief
Get on that boat!

                              Chef
There's nothing on it, man!

                              Chief
Get on that boat!

Chef starts down into the Vietnamese sampan. He is
really pissed off. He shoves the Vietnamese men out
of the way.

                              Chef
     (to man)
Move it, asshole.

The Chief watches as Chef goes through the routine
of examining the sampan and what it carries. He is
very nervous as he looks in all the baskets.

                              Chef
Pigs! Mangoes!

                              Chief
What's in the rice bag?

                              Chef
Fucking rice!

                              Chief
Well, look in there, Chef!

                              Chef
Fucking fish! More coconuts. Rice. Here's
rice.

                              Chief
What's in that vegetable basket?

Chef moves deeper into the sampan. He looks at
the Vietnamese girl that is sitting on a yellow
can.

                    Chef
     (to girl)
     Can couc! Come on! Get out of there.

He grabs her and roughly pulls her out of the interior of the cabin. He moves into it and starts
looking around.

                    Chief
     Check that vegetable basket.

                    Chef
     All right!

One of the Vietnamese men starts to protest.

                    Clean
     Shut up, slope!

                    Chef
     There ain't nothing in here.

                    Chief
     What's in the boxes? Look in that tin can.
     That rusty can.

                    Chef
     Just fucking rice, that's all! There ain't
     nothing in it!

                    Chief
     Check that yellow can. She was sitting on
     it. What's in it?

Chef starts for it. All of a sudden, the girl

moves. Clean opens up with the M60. She is blown apart, falling back on the deck.

In an instant, THEY ALL OPEN FIRE. One of the Vietnamese men is blown apart into the water, and the other two men are gunned down in their tracks.

All of them continue to fire their rifles and guns wildly, yelling obscenities. Willard has his .45 out but does not shoot.

                    Clean
    Motherfuckers!

                Chef (weeping)
    Let's kill them all!

                    Lance
    Fucking cocksucker mothers!

Finally the Chief calls out to them.

                    Chief
    Hold it! Hold it!

They all stop firing, but Chef, Lance, and Clean are all mumbling hysterically.

                    Chef
    Let's kill all the assholes!

                    Chief
    Chef, hold it! Hold it!

                    Chef
        (hysterical)
    . . . why not?

                    Chief
Clean?

                    Clean
I'm good.

                    Chief
You okay, Lance?

                    Lance
Shit! Fuck!

                    Chief
Chef?

Chef has moved to the yellow can that the Vietnamese girl was sitting on. He opens the lid and checks what she had hidden.

                    Chef
Look what she was hiding. See what she was running for?

He reaches inside of the can, and pulls out a PUPPY. They all react.

                    Chef
A fucking puppy! A puppy.

                    Lance
Gimme that dog! Gimme that dog!

                    Chef
No, you're not gonna get it! Give me the fucking dog, asshole!

Lance grabs the dog from him, kicking Chef back. Chef throws a mango at him.

                         Chef
          Fuck you! Fucking mango, too! You want that?

The Vietnamese girl, still alive and bleeding,
moves behind Chef.

                        Chief
          Chef, she's moving behind you. She's alive.
          Check her out.

Chef turns and bends down to her.

                         Chef
          Come on, Clean, goddamnit, give me a hand!

Clean jumps down into the sampan. He and Chef
pick up the girl and carry her to the edge of the
boat.

                        Chief
          She's not dead. She's moving.
            (to group)
          Let's take it easy. Take it easy. Slow down
          and take it easy.

                        Clean
          Bring her up.

                        Chief
          Is she breathing, Chef?

                         Chef
          She's hurt. She's bleeding.

                        Chief
          Bring her onboard. We're taking her to an
          ARVN.

ANOTHER ANGLE TO INCLUDE WILLARD

Willard looks at the girl and then to the Chief.

> **Willard**
> What are you talking about?

> **Chief**
> We're taking her to some friendlies. She's
> wounded, she's not dead.

Willard holds his .45. Looks down at Chef and the
girl.

> **Willard**
> Get out of there, Chef.

> **Chief**
> The book says, Captain—

Before anybody can react, Willard aims and SHOOTS
THE GIRL DEAD with his .45. She falls dead in Chef's
arms.

> **Chef**
> Fuck you. Fuck them.

Willard turns and looks at the Chief.

> **Willard**
> I told you not to stop. Now let's go.

FADE OUT:

FADE IN:

EXT. THE RIVER—PBR—EVENING

The boat moves up the river.

> **Willard (V.O.)**
> It was a way we had over here of living with
> ourselves. We'd cut them in half with a
> machine gun, and give them a Band-Aid. It
> was a lie. And the more I saw of them, the
> more I hated liars. Those boys were never
> gonna look at me the same way again, but I
> felt like I knew one or two things about
> Kurtz, that weren't in the dossier.

EXT. DO LUNG BRIDGE—THE PBR—RIVER—NIGHT

The boat edges in toward a wrecked bridge in the
distance. Along the banks are sandbagged fortifications with the U.S. soldiers. There is a
bright fire burning uncontrolled in the distance—in fact there are several—flame and sparks
from welding on the bridge momentarily light up
the night. There is sporadic gunfire at O.S.
snipers, and flares arc through the sky above
the bridge.

> **Willard (V.O.)**
> Do Lung bridge was the last army outpost on
> the Nung River. Beyond it there was only
> Kurtz.

ANGLE FORWARD—LANCE AND CHEF

They are in full combat gear. Lance looks ahead,
reacting to the pyrotechnics. The puppy is in front
of him. Chef walks up and squats down beside him.

                    Chef
Hey, Lance, what do you think?

                    Lance
It's beautiful.

                    Chef
What's the matter with you? You're acting
kind of weird.

                    Lance
You know that last tab of acid I was saving?

                    Chef
Yeah.

                    Lance
I dropped it.

                    Chef
You dropped acid? Far out.

ANOTHER ANGLE

The Chief powers the boat forward, as Willard and
Clean watch in awe.

Everywhere are wrecked boats, parts of jeeps
sticking out of the water—a smashed helicopter on
the banks. The bridge is in a state of siege.
Mortars and rockets arc through the night indiscriminately and rip through the nearby jungle.
Light automatic WEAPON FIRE is HEARD occasionally. The entire scene is lit by parachute
flares.

As the PBR edges forward, SOLDIERS run up through

the water, trying to get aboard. One soldier is carrying some luggage and an M16. He splashes into the water, in a mad dash for freedom.

Soldier
Take me home! Goddamn you!

Chief
Get away from this boat.

Soldier #2
You'll get what you deserve!

He and the others are left behind as the PBR continues forward. Willard sees a young LIEU-TENANT kneeling on a platform that juts out into the water. He is holding a small strobe light, trying to signal the PBR down. He is holding a large mail bag and a pouch in the other hand.

Willard motions toward the shore. The Chief turns the boat towards the lieutenant.

Carlson
Is there a Captain Willard on board? Captain Willard?

Willard
Yeah! Who's that?

As the boat crosses to a stop, Lance swings the spotlight onto the lieutenant.

Carlson
Lieutenant Carlson, sir.
(to Lance)
Get that light off me!

Lance swings the light off him, as Willard squats down on the bow of the boat.

Carlson

I was sent here from Nha Trang with these three days ago, sir. Expected you here a little sooner.

He hands Willard a plastic bag with maximum security markings. Willard takes it—also a mail pouch.

Carlson

This is mail for the boat. You don't know how happy this makes me, sir.

Willard

Why?

Carlson

Now I can get out of here, if I can find a way.

He turns and splashes off into the darkness. Then stops and looks back.

Carlson

You're in the asshole of the world, Captain!

He salutes, then turns and moves away. Willard hops off the side of the boat into the mud, moving up toward the shore.

Chief

Captain, where you going?

Willard

To see if I can find some fuel and get some information. Pick me up the other side of the bridge.

                              Chief
                    (to his men)
               Somebody go with him.
                    (to Chef)
               Chef.

Chef doesn't move, not wanting to go. No one budges,
then Lance volunteers.

                              Lance
               I'll go. I want to go.

He picks up the puppy and an M16, then jumps over
the side onto the shore.

EXT. SHORE—NIGHT

As Willard and Lance walk across an open area,
they are lit by the battle in the background.
Lance looks up and around dreamily as he follows
Willard. They move up the embankment and along a
barbed wire on the edge of the road. SHELLS SCREAM
overhead. Lance just stands looking down on the
phantasmagoric strings of lights, the smoke, the
fires.

Willard jumps down into a trench. We SEE a SOLDIER
crouched, holding his buddy, who is crying uncon-
trollably.

                            Willard
               Where can I find the C.O.?

                            Soldier
               You came right to it, son of a bitch!

                            Willard
               Lance! Get down here!

Lance is still reacting to the pyrotechnics around him. He turns and jumps down into the trench.

                    Willard
You still got a commanding officer here?

                    Soldier
Beverly Hills.

                    Willard
What?

                    Soldier
Right up the road there's a concrete bunker called Beverly Hills. Where the fuck else do you think it would be?

Willard turns and moves away from the two soldiers. Lance follows.

The CAMERA FOLLOWS them as they proceed down the long trench. They pass a group of black G.I.s. Suddenly Willard trips over a body, and falls right into a mud puddle. The body stirs.

                    Soldier
You stepped in my face!

                    Lance
We thought you were dead.

                    Soldier
Well, you thought wrong, damnit!

They come to another gun emplacement, where two BLACK SOLDIERS are at a fifty-caliber machine gun. The GUNNER blasts away into the night, walking and swearing at the Vietcong. The SPOTTER is feeding

the bullets into the gun. Psychedelic guitar music
plays on a portable radio.

Gunner
(to enemy)
I told you to stop fucking with me! You
think you're so bad, huh, nigga?

Willard watches for a while, then shouts over to
him.

Willard
What are you shooting at, soldier?

Gunner
Gooks! What the fuck do you think I'm shooting at?
*(turns and sees it's an
officer)*
I'm sorry, sir. There are gooks out there
by the wire. But I think I killed them
all.

Spotter
You ain't shot shit! Listen!

The enemy's yelling continues.

Gunner
Oh, shit, he's trying to call his friends.
Send up a flare.

The spotter reaches over and picks up a flare pistol,
and fires a FLARE into the air. The gunner starts
blasting away again.

Gunner
You think you so bad, nigga? You think you
so bad?

He stops firing. The yelling continues.

> **Spotter**
> They're all dead, stupid. There's one still
> alive underneath them bodies.

> **Willard**
> Who's the commanding officer here?

> **Gunner**
> Ain't you?
> *(to enemy)*
> You think you so bad? I got something for
> your ass! I got something for you now!

Lance climbs up on top of the sandbags with the
puppy and looks out at the pyrotechnics. Explosions
go off all around him . . . space city.

> **Spotter**
> There's nothing but bodies, man!

> **Gunner**
> *(to spotter)*
> Go get the Roach, man. Go get the Roach,
> nigga!

The spotter moves down the trench, to where a
tall, lanky black soldier wearing all sorts of
beads and trinkets leans against the ditch, sleeping.

> **Spotter**
> *(calling out)*
> Roach. Roach!

THE ROACH gets up somewhat annoyed, but very cool,
and saunters up toward the machine gun. Willard
looks over and sees Lance up on top of the sandbags.

Willard

Lance!

Lance climbs down back into the trench. The Roach and spotter move back to the machine gun, where the gunner waits. The Roach turns off the radio, sits down, and listens.

Spotter

Do you hear them? Well, bust them!

Vietcong (O.S.)

Hey, G.I., fuck you!

Gunner

You hear him out there on the wire, man?

Roach

Yeah.

Vietcong (O.S.)

Fuck you, you G.I.

Gunner

You need a flare?

Roach

No.
  (listens)
He's close, man. He's real close.

Vietcong (O.S.)

G.I., fuck you!

The Roach opens the breech of his shotgunlike weapon, plunks a big slug into it. He snaps it closed, then turns and wraps the strap around his arm. He points the weapon up into the air—he listens to the YELLING, calculating, then fires. The grenade whistles off into the night. There is a sharp EXPLOSION that cuts off the scream. Then the thud of bodies.

                    Roach
    Motherfucker.

                    Willard
    Hey, soldier. Do you know who's in command here?

                    Roach
    Yeah.

He turns and walks away.

                                        CUT TO:

FULL SHOT—PBR—BRIDGE

The PBR stands in the shallows. Chef, the Chief, and Clean are waiting for Willard and Lance. SHELLS WHISTLE BY and CRASH in the distance as the welding continues on the bridge.

Clean looks up and sees a direct hit on the bridge. TWO SOLDIERS are blown off one of the towers and into the water.

                    Clean
    Holy shit! Yo, Chief, two guys just got blown off that bridge.

                    Chief
    You hang on, man. You're gonna be okay.

Clean turns and moves to the bow, where Chef is kneeling by the mail bag.

What's that?

Chef
Mail, man!

Chief
Later on the mail! Watch them trees.

Willard and Lance climb back onto the boat, loaded down with supplies. They move down into the PBR.

Willard
There's no diesel fuel, but I picked up some ammo. Let's move out.

Chief
Did you find the C.O., Captain?

Willard
There's no fucking C.O. here. Let's just get going.

Chief
Which way, Captain?

Willard
You know which way, Chief.

He takes off his shirt, then his T-shirt.

Chief
You're on your own, Captain. Still want to go on? Like this bridge. We build it every night, Charlie blows it right back up again, just so the generals can say the road's open. Think about it . . . who cares?

                    Willard
Just get us up river!

                    Chief
Chef. On the bow.
  (to Clean)
Stand by, Clean.

FULL VIEW—THE PBR—NIGHT

The men on the bridge continue to weld with their
torches as the PBR backs up, then the Chief pulls
away from the bridge. They all look back in the
distance, the hills flash with charges, there is a
fiery glow, the concussion of heavy explosions, as
the BRIDGE BLOWS.

                                    DISSOLVE TO:

EXT. RIVER—THE PBR—DAY

It is the next morning. The PBR continues on its
journey up river. Chef distributes mail from the
mail bag.

                    Chef
Shit, you got another one, Clean!

                    Clean
No shit. Wait a minute. Is that it?

                    Chef
That's it for you. Lance? Mr. L. B. Johnson,
there you go.

Lance takes the letter.

> **Lance**
> Far out, man! All right, I been waiting for this one.

> **Chef**
> *(to all)*
> I got another one. I got a box from Eva.

> **Lance**
> *(reading)*
> "Lance, I'm fine. Sue and I went tripping in Disneyland. Sue skinned her knee."

> **Chef**
> Man, I'm gonna get back to Antoine's.

> **Lance**
> *(to letter)*
> How could I fucking forget, man? Beautiful!
> *(reading)*
> "There could never be a place like Disneyland, or could there? Let me know."
> *(looking around)*
> Jim, it's here. It really is here.

Willard has opened the Top Secret pouch and is reading the letter inside:

> **Willard**
> *(reading)*
> "There's been a new development regarding your mission, which we must now communicate to you.

> **Willard**
> "Months ago, a man was ordered on a mission, which was identical to yours. We

132

have reason to believe that he is now operating with Colonel Kurtz. Saigon was carrying him MIA for his family's sake, but they assumed he was dead. Then they intercepted a letter he tried to send to his wife."

"Find someone else. Forget it. I'm never coming back."

Willard
Captain Richard Colby. He was with Kurtz.

Lance
(to himself)
Disneyland. Fuck, man, this is better than Disneyland!

Chef
(reading newspaper)
". . . Charles Miller Manson ordered the slaughter of all in the home anyway, as a symbol of protest." That's really weird, ain't it?

Lance has taken some SMOKE BOMBS and is popping them open. COLORED SMOKE begins to pour out.

Lance
Purple Haze! Look!

Chief
Lance, put that smoke away.

Clean
I got a tape from my mom.

Lance is playing with the smoking flares.

Lance

Chief, rainbow reality, man. Get a good whiff.

Chef

Eva can't picture me in Vietnam. She pictures me at home, having a beer, watching TV.

The colored smoke is getting in everybody's eyes. The whole boat is enveloped.

Clean

Hey, Lance, man!

Lance

(to himself)
Hot potato! Hot potato!

Chef

Eva's not sure she can have a relationship with me. Here I am, thirteen thousand fucking miles away, trying to keep a relationship with my ass.

Clean's tape from his mom is PLAYING.

Clean's Mother (Over Tape)

". . . and that's much more than I can say for some of your friends. If this tape is any good, I will have Dad and the family send you a tape of their own."

SUDDENLY streams of TRACERS whip out of the jungle at them, other bullets smash and ricochet off the deck; glass shatters, everybody jumps to their battle stations.

Lance jumps into the turret of the twin fifties and starts blasting away at the jungle. The Chief tries to power the PBR out of the ambush. Clean jumps up behind the M60 machine gun and starts firing. Chef gets behind the M50 gun and starts firing. Willard uses his M16.

Everything is confusion, yelling, gunfire, the thud of bullets ripping into the PBR fiberglass hull. Lance's guns return fire. He screams obscenities as he vents an almost superhuman violence.

MED. CLOSE SHOT—LANCE—FIRING HIS GUNS

Turning in the turret; bullets smash and explode around him. Nobody quite knows where the fire is coming from.

VIEW ON THE CHIEF

The Chief steers and accelerates erratically, try-ing to dodge the fire fight.

VIEW ON CLEAN FIRING HIS GUN

Firing the M60 . . . suddenly it jams. As he rises up behind the shield he is riddled by machine gun fire. The bullets blast into his throat, chest, stomach . . . he falls to the deck.

Nobody has seen that he is down yet. They keep fir-ing their guns into the jungle. The Chief throttles forward, the boat surges ahead and slams out across the river. It is all over very quickly.

The Chief turns and sees that Clean has been hit and is down on the deck.

Chief

Chef! Take care of Clean! Captain, Clean's hit! He's hit!

Lance climbs out of the gun turret and looks around for the little puppy.

Lance

Where'd the dog go? Where's the dog? We gotta go back and get the dog!

Chef crawls to Clean and turns him over. Sees that he is dead.

Chef

Clean! Hey! Bubber, you can't die! You fucker! Hey, Bubber!

Clean's Mother (Over Tape)

"...hoping that pretty soon, not too soon ...but pretty soon..."

Lance takes over the wheel as Chief turns and stares at Clean's body in horror. He feels Clean's blood on his hand.

Clean's Mother (Over Tape)

"I'll have a lot of grandchildren to love and spoil, and then, when your wife gets them back, she'll be mad with me. Even Aunt Jessie and Mama will come to celebrate your coming home. Granny and Dad are trying to get enough money to get you a car. But don't tell them, because that's our secret. Anyhow..."

Clean lying dead, flat on his back. Chief turns him over and holds his wrist to try and take his pulse.

Clean's Mother (Over Tape)

". . . do the right thing, stay out of the way of the bullets, and bring your hiney home all in one piece . . . 'cause we love you very much. Love, Mom."

Chief is holding Clean's hand and crying.

DISSOLVE TO:

EXT. RIVER—THE PBR—DAY

The boat under power, moving through fog. They pass downed jets, wreckage, burning fires. Willard is sitting on the bow, looking out into the distance as though he sees something.

Willard
(motions to Chief)
Hold on. Throw me the glasses.

He looks through the binoculars.

WILLARD'S POV—WRECKED FRENCH PLANTATION—DAY

In the distance, we can make out a PLANTATION. The dock has been devastated by years of fighting. There is a heavy FOG or MIST everywhere. Up on the hill above the dock sits a large house; it does not look heavily damaged.

EXT. RIVER—THE PBR—DAY

Willard picks up his M16 and moves to the front of the boat. Chief has also seen the wrecked plantation.

Chief

Lance. Get the 16 on the bow.
(to Chef)
Chef, on the 60.

The Chief pulls the PBR slowly up to the wrecked dock. Willard jumps off with his M16 in hand and cautiously looks around.

He walks into a wrecked barn. He comes out the side and makes his way back to Chef and Lance, who are standing on the dock.

Chief

Lance, cover the captain.

Suddenly from out of the fog...FRENCH VOICES shout out.

LaFavre

You are surrounded. Return. Drop your weapons.

Chef

(in French)
Don't shoot! Don't shoot!
(to Lance and others)
They're French.
(in French, to soldiers)
I am dropping my weapon!

Chef and Lance start to put down their M16s, the Chief shouts out furiously from the boat

Chief

Chef! Pick up that weapon! Pick it up! Stand fast!

Chef continues to shout to the French.

Chef

We are Americans! We are friends!

LaFavre

Drop your weapons!

As Willard walks down the dock, French soldiers appear out of the fog, totally surrounding them. Willard stops in front of them, realizing there is no way out, and raises his rifle in surrender.

Chief
(to Lance and Chef)
All right, you men. Put down your weapons.

They all drop their weapons. More soldiers step out.

Chef
(in French)
We are Americans. We are friends. We are friends.

We SEE more French and Cambodian soldiers as they step out of the fog onto the dock. They move forward cautiously. It is strange. It is like meeting up with a group of soldiers from the French Indo-Chinese War. It's as though they've stepped into 1954. The soldiers are still wearing parts of the red berets of their particular unit that fought against the Viet Minh. There are also Vietnamese who serve the French and who fought with the French. They all bear older automatic weapons and suspicion in their eyes.

Another Frenchman joins the group. This is obviously the patriarch of the family. HUBERT DEMARAIS is about fifty, with a dignity and strength about him. He and Willard look at each other.

Willard

We lost one of our men.

Demarais

We French always pay respect to the dead of our allies. You're all welcome.

   (pause)

My name is Hubert DeMarais. This is my family's plantation. It has been such for seventy years, and it will be such until we are all dead.

DISSOLVE TO:

EXT. GRAVEYARD—DOLLY SHOT—DAY

The group is assembled. There is a platoon of Cambodian soldiers standing by an open grave, SERGEANT LAFAVRE in front of them.

LaFavre

To my command! Attention! Weapons on the shoulder! Present weapons!

The platoon present their weapons, as Clean's body is carried toward the grave. The bugler brings the bugle up to his lips and plays "Taps."

Willard looks up and sees something on the balcony of the house.

HIS POV:

A young WOMAN, dressed in white, is on the balcony. She has been watching the ceremony. She turns back into the house.

The Chief bends down and picks up the tattered American flag, which is on Clean's body. Lance places Clean's tape recorder on the body. The body is lowered into the grave.

Chief
(to Willard)
Captain, accept the flag of Tyrone Miller, on behalf of a grateful nation.

He hands the folded flag to Willard.

INT. DINING ROOM—GROUP—NIGHT

We SEE the DeMarais interior. They have set up a table for the crew, and with some of their own enlisted men. The table is headed by Sergeant LaFavre, who is already seriously into the wine.

A waiter comes to the table and stops next to Chef. He is holding a plate full of chicken, etc. Chef's face lights up as he regards the wonderful European-style food.

Chef
This food is really wonderful, isn't it? The wine, the sauces. I can't believe it. Can I speak with the chef?

LaFavre
The chef speaks only Vietnamese.

Chef
No kidding. He cooks like this and he can't even speak French?
(to Lance)
Hey, Lance, the chef's a slope.

Lance has been loading up on food from the waiter's plate. As the waiter moves away from him, Lance reaches across the table for the bread and accidentally knocks over a glass.

Chief
Hey, Lance . . .

Lance realizes he is eating like an animal, sits back down.

The VIEW MOVES ALONG THE TABLE AND REVEALS that on a higher level there is a more elaborate table set, where the DeMarais family is dining with Willard.

Willard is sitting next to DeMarais, who is at the head of the table. Christian, ANNE-MARIE, and old blind UNCLE, Claudine, the TUTOR, and Philippe are all seated, listening to one of the grandchildren, who is reciting a poem. The other grandchildren stand nearby listening.

The child stumbles through the poem.

Demarais
(in French)
You still need to study with Mr. Robert. Let's go. Not too bad. Go to bed everyone now.

The children kiss their parents good night, and run out of the room. DeMarais turns to Willard.

DESMARAIS
This is Baudelaire. It is a very cruel poem for children, but they need it, because life sometime is very cruel.

He reaches behind him and picks up a plaque, hands
it to Willard.

                    Demarais
As you can see. Attack repels by the family.

                    Philippe
Just for this war.

                    Demarais
          (pointing to the plaque)
Viet Cong, fifty-eight. North Vietnamese,
twelve. South Vietnamese, eleven.

                    Willard
Americans, six?

                    Demarais
Yes, well, there were perhaps mistakes.

Willard hands the plaque back to DeMarais, who hands
it off to Philippe.

ANOTHER ANGLE TO INCLUDE ROXANNE

The young woman we saw earlier, ROXANNE, has come
down the stairs and moves into the dining room.
DeMarais looks up and sees her.

                    Demarais
          (in French)
Roxanne, you were curious to see these
Americans, weren't you?

                    Roxanne
          (in French)
No, I was only hungry.

She stops in front of an empty chair next to Philippe. Willard rises to greet her.

Demarais
May I present Captain Willard, he is of a paratroop regiment. Madame Sarrault.

She smiles and indicates for Willard to sit down.

Roxanne
Captain.

She sits down. There is an uneasy silence. She laughs slightly.

Roxanne
(in French)
"An angel passes . . ."

DeMarais reacts.

Demarais
(in French)
". . . Let's butcher it!" Do you remember the story in Paris, when the baron said, "Let's cut the angel?"

Roxanne
(in French)
I don't think that is the subject tonight.

Demarais
I'm sorry, Captain. It was just a little story. And people starving during the war. They are all around the table, and there was a silence, somebody say, "An angel is passing by." So somebody say, "Let's eat it!"
(laughs)

Willard

How long can you possibly stay here?

Demarais

We stay forever.

Willard

No, no, I mean, why don't you go back home to France?

Demarais

This is our home, Captain.

Willard

Sooner or later, you're—

Demarais

No!

Roxanne interrupts, says something to him in French. He silences her.

Demarais
(to Willard)
You don't understand our mentality! The French officer mentality! At first, we lose in Second World War. I don't say that you Americans win, but we lose.

Claudine

Oh, Papa.

DeMarais is starting to get heated up.

Demarais

When I speak, you shut up!
(to Willard)
In Dien Bien Phu, we lose! In Algeria, we

lose! In Indochina, we lose! But here, we
don't lose! This piece of earth, we keep it!
We will never lose it! Never!

The OLD BLIND UNCLE at the other end of the table
speaks, as Claudine cuts his food for him and feeds
him.

Old Uncle

The Americans, in 1945, yeah, after the
Japanese war, your President Roosevelt
didn't want the French people to stay in
Indochina. So you Americans implant the Viet
Minh.

Willard

(to DeMarais)
What's he mean?

Demarais

Yeah, that's true. The Vietcong were
invented by the Americans, sir.

Willard

The Americans?

Old Uncle

And now you take the French place, and the
Viet Minh fight you. And what can you do?
Nothing. Absolutely nothing.

Demarais

The Vietnamese are very intelligent. You
never know what they think. The Russian ones
who help them, "Come and give us their money,
we are all Communists. Chinese, come and give
us guns. We're all brothers." They hate the
Chinese! Maybe they hate the American less
than the Russian and the Chinese. If to-

morrow the Vietnamese are Communists, they
will be Vietnamese Communists. And this is
something that you never understood, you
American.

Old Uncle
I don't know. Maybe in the future we can
make something with the Viet Minh.

Philippe
Don't you understand? The V.C. say, "Go
away! Go away!" That's finish for all the
white people in Indochina. If you're French,
American, that's all the same. "Go!" They
want to forget you. Look, Captain—

He rises from the table.

Demarais
Come on, Philippe. It's enough now.

Philippe goes and picks up an egg from a basket,
returns to the table.

Philippe
Look, this is the truth . . .

He breaks the egg in his hand, the contents dribble
out.

Philippe
An egg, the white leaves, but the yellow
stays!

He turns and walks away.

Demarais
(in French)
Come on, stay with us. What's going on?

Philippe
(calling back)
They don't want to face the truth.

He points to the dining room, turns and exits.
LaFavre, playing his accordion, walks toward the
dining room.

Christian
When I was in Saigon, I spoke to an American
politician, and he explained it very well. He
said, "Look. Yesterday it was Korea, today
Vietnam, tomorrow Thailand, the Philippines,
then maybe Europe."

LaFavre enters, playing the accordion.

Christian
Come on, why not Europe? Look what happened
in Czechoslovakia recently. And even before
the Second World War, the Americans knew
exactly what was going on! They don't want
that shit to take over!
(to LaFavre, who is play-
ing the accordion)
LaFavre! LaFavre, stop it!

LaFavre
All you white people are shit.

Christian
They are fighting. Fighting for freedom.

LaFavre
Freedom? Bullshit. French bullshit. American
bullshit.
(to all)
Dien Bien Phu, that serious! All soldier
know they are already dead.

LaFavre

(to Willard)

You know anything about Dien Bien Phu?

Willard

Yeah, I know.

Demarais

No, you don't. Not really.

Tutor

A military mistake.

Demarais

A mistake? A voluntary mistake! Voluntary!

LaFavre

All the soldiers knew, we knew we would be dead.

Demarais

The generals and the colonels believe it's impossible for the Viets to get the cannon up there in the mountain. But they do. Then they wait for the rain to come. When it comes, no airplane can fly there, and our paratroopers jump at ninety meters! I mean, you know, ninety meters! Seventy meters! That's crazy! Nobody in the world can do that! And they only do that to be dead with their friends.

LaFavre starts playing "The Star Spangled Banner."

Demarais

The French Army was sacrificed. Sacrificed by the politicians safe at home. They put the army in an impossible situation where they couldn't win!

Tutor
You exaggerate.

Demarais
The students are marching in Paris, protesting, demonstrating. They stab the soldiers in their back! The soldier would open a grenade, it wouldn't work. A piece of paper would fall, "Union of the French Woman." "We are for the Viets." Traitors! Communist traitors at home!

LaFavre
Dien Bien Phu, okay. The French is shit. No one care. No one want to—

Christian
You are bothering me, LaFavre!
  (to Willard)
Why don't you Americans learn from us, from our mistakes? My God, with your army, your strength, your power . . . you could win if you wanted to!

As LaFavre leaves, he falls down some steps that lead out of the dining room.

Demarais
  (in French; to Christian)
Be kind and help this poor LaFavre who fell, please.

Christian
  (to Willard)
You can win!

He rises and goes to help the sergeant. As they leave, his wife Anne-Marie sits there nervously, then rises, excusing herself.

                         Old Uncle
You know, I'm sure we can make something here. I'm sure about it, you know? I never do something wrong to the people here.

                          Tutor
That's right, but the Communist at home have never been traitors.

                        Demarais
No, never traitors. For me, Mendes-France was a Communist.

                          Tutor
Mendes-France was a socialist.

                        Demarais
He was a Communist! That's it!

They get into an argument in French. The others look at each other, at Willard, as the argument continues.

                          Tutor
Socialist.

                        Demarais
How do you want the government to win when it is Communist?

                          Tutor
Communists have always worked for peace wherever they are.

Demarais

They killed the French Army, which was the strongest. Destroyed because of who? The Communists.

Tutor

The army damaged itself by its attitude toward the people here.

Demarais

And why do you think that it did that? Because it understood it had been sacrificed by the Communist government!

Tutor

Socialist.

Demarais

Communist!

Tutor

Captain, good night.

The tutor gets up and starts to walk out . . . gives DeMarais one more shot.

Tutor
(to DeMarais)
Mendes-France was a Socialist.

He leaves.

Old Uncle

We can stay. I know that we can stay. You know, we always helped the people, we work with the people.

The old man continues babbling, as Claudine helps him up.

Claudine

Come on, we are leaving.

Old Uncle

So we can be friends, we are agreed.

They exit, Claudine consoling him. Now only Roxanne, Willard, and DeMarais are at the table.

Demarais

See, Captain, when my grandfather and my uncle's father came here, there was nothing. Nothing. The Vietnamese were nothing. So we worked hard, very hard, and brought the rubber from Brazil, and then plant it here. We took the Vietnamese, work with them, make something, something out of nothing. So when you ask me why we want to stay here, Captain, we want to stay here because it's ours, it belongs to us. It keeps our family together. We fight for that! While you Americans, you are fighting for the biggest nothing in history. I'm sorry, Captain. I will see if your men needs any help to repair your boat, so that you can go on with <u>your</u> war. Good night, Roxanne.

He rises from the table and moves out of the room. Willard and Roxanne are left alone at the table.

Roxanne

I apologize for my family, Captain. We have all lost much here. Hubert—his wife and two sons. And I have lost a husband.

Willard

I understand.

Roxanne

You are tired of the war. I can see it in
your face. It was the same in the eyes of
the soldiers of our war. We called them
"Les Soldat Perdus." The Lost Soldiers.
   (beat)
If you like we can have some cognac.

She rises and moves to the living room.

Willard

No, I have to see about my men and . . .

Roxanne stops at the bottom of the stairs. She
turns to look at him.

Roxanne

The war will be still here tomorrow.

Willard

Yeah, I guess you're right.

He rises and walks down into the living room.
Roxanne moves toward a table full of liquor bottles.

Roxanne

I noticed you had no wine at dinner.

She begins to pour some cognac into a glass.

Willard

No, I don't drink wine. I do like cognac,
but I don't want any now, thank you.

Roxanne

Well, then I must drink alone then.

She picks up her glass of cognac, and walks by
Willard out onto the terrace. Stops and looks back
at him.

Roxanne
Will you go back after the war to America?

Willard
No.

Roxanne
Then you're like us, your home is here.

She walks farther out onto the terrace, sits down
on a sofa, with her back to the river below.
Willard follows her and stands next to her at the
railing. We can SEE the men working on the PBR down
below at the dock.

Roxanne
Do you know why you can never step into the
same river twice?

Willard
Yeah. Because it's always moving.

DISSOLVE TO:

INT. ROXANNE'S BEDROOM—NIGHT

Our VIEW starts CLOSE on Roxanne's hands. She is
holding a long opium pipe. In the other hand she
holds a long tamper with some opium on the end. She
handles it expertly over a small lamp with open
flame, heating it, then putting the bead of opium
into the pipe.

Roxanne

I used to prepare a pipe for my husband. It
was the morphine he took for the wounds he
suffered in his heart.

She looks over at Willard. They are both lying on
her bed, next to each other.

Roxanne

He would rage and he would cry, my lost soldier.
And I said to him, "There are two of you, don't
you see? One that kills and one that loves." And
he said to me, "I don't know whether I am an
animal or a god." But you are both.

She offers him the pipe, he takes it and inhales
the smoke from the opium, gives it back to her. She
smokes also.

Roxanne

You want more?

He shakes his head.

Roxanne

All that matters is that you are alive. You
are alive, Captain. That's the truth.

She gets up from the bed, unties one of the strings
of the bed canopy, and takes off her robe, revealing
her naked body. She walks around the bed, untying the
other strings. She approaches him. He reaches up to
her.

Roxanne

There are two of you, don't you see? One
that kills . . . and one that loves.

EXT. RIVER—PBR—DAY

Mist swells up and around the river as the boat moves into an obscure FOG. Willard is up front on the bow, trying to see what's ahead. The Chief is at the helm.

MED. CLOSE SHOT—THE CHIEF

We catch glimpses of him, even though we are in the fog, he can't see a thing. Finally he shuts down the engine and they coast.

> **Chief**
> Can't see nothing. We're stopping.

Willard jumps up and moves to the Chief.

> **Willard**
> You're not authorized to stop this boat, Chief.

> **Chief**
> I said I can't see a thing, Captain! I'm stopping this boat! I ain't risking no more lives!

> **Willard**
> I'm in command here, goddamnit. You'll do what I say!

> **Chief**
> *(to Chef)*
> You see anything, Chef?

Chef is at the back of the boat behind the M50. He searches the banks.

> Chef
>
> Why don't they fucking attack, man?

ANGLE ON LANCE

His head back, wailing eerily.

> Chef
>
> Watch it over here, Chief. Got a stump.

> Chief
>
> Lance. On the fifties.

ANGLE ON THE PBR

We catch glimpses through the moving FOG, of all the men on the PBR, at their guns, searching the shoreline.

> Willard (V.O.)
>
> He was close. He was real close. I couldn't see him yet, but I could feel him, as if the boat were being sucked up river and the water was flowing back into the jungle. Whatever was going to happen, it wasn't going to be the way they called it back in Nha Trang.

SUDDENLY the air is filled with ARROWS, an avalanche of arrows in the sky. They come down clattering on the deck. Chef opens fire.

> Willard
>
> Arrows!

Chief
Fire! Chef, open up! Fire! Lance! Fire!

ANOTHER ANGLE—ARROWS

Arrows everywhere, primitive spears flung expertly.

ANGLE ON LANCE

In the front turret, arrows whiz around him. He turns, smiles, picks one up, looks at it, breaks it in half.

ANGLE ON THE CHEF

Frightened, but almost heroic, firing his weapon and shouting obscenities at the weird, dancing heathens attacking him. Arrows fall harmlessly around him.

HIGH ANGLE—THE SKY

Thousands of arrows in the sky come clattering down on the deck by the Chief.

ANGLE TO GO WITH WILLARD

Amazed . . . immediately he knows they're harmless, done more to frighten than to injure. But still, he's never seen anything like this in all his time in Vietnam, and he knows in his gut that it is still another message from Kurtz. He moves to Chef, tries to make him stop firing.

Willard

Chef! Chef, it's okay! Quit firing! They're just little toy arrows. Cut it out! Quiet! Chief, tell them to hold their fire! They're just little sticks! They're trying to scare us!

The Chief picks up his M16 and turns to Willard wildly.

Chief

You got us into this mess, and now you can't get us out, because you don't know where the hell you're going, do you?
  (no answer)
Do you? You son of a bitch! You bastard!

The Chief leaves the wheel of the PBR and steps up on the deck with his M16.

Willard

(shouting to Lance)
Lance, get the wheel!

Lance moves to take over the wheel, as Chief starts firing his M16 madly.

Chief

You savages! Come and get it, you son of a bitches!

He drops the spent M16, moves to the M60 machine gun and starts firing madly again.

Suddenly the Chief stops short, puzzled, a small droplet of blood lines his mouth. He coughs up a mouthful of blood, then he looks down. The head of a SPEAR has gone through his chest. He looks up at Willard.

Chief

A spear?

He remains looking directly into Willard's eyes, then starts to fall. Willard catches him, and is pulled down to the deck by the weight of the Chief's body. The Chief looks up at him and suddenly reaches his hands for Willard's throat, trying to pull Willard down on top of the spearhead, trying to skewer him, and pull him along with him to death. A beat as they struggle, then suddenly the Chief DIES.

EXT. RIVER—THE PBR—DAY

Lance is putting camouflage paint on the Chief.

Willard has jumped off the boat with all of his gear. Chef looks down at him.

Willard

My mission is to make it up into Cambodia. There's a Green Beret colonel up there who's gone insane, and I'm supposed to kill him.

Chef

That's fucking typical! Shit! Fucking Vietnam mission! I'm short and we gotta go up there so you can kill one of our own guys? That's fucking great! That's just fucking great, man! Shit! That's fucking crazy! I thought you were going in to blow up a bridge, or some fucking railroad tracks, or something!

Lance has pulled the Chief's body into the river, and jumped in himself. Willard and Chef watch him, as he tries to bury Chief's body in the water.

Willard turns to leave.

                    Willard
      That's all right.

                     Chef
      No, wait. We'll go together. On the boat.
      We'll go with you. We'll go out there. But
      on the boat, okay?

Lance gently floats the Chief off downstream. We SEE
the Chief's body slowly disappear.

                                    DISSOLVE TO:

EXT. RIVER—PBR—NIGHT

The PBR moves up-river. The shore is lit up with
burning torches and a large wooden structure in
flames. We SEE the faces of the remaining crew, as
they take in this sight.

                                    DISSOLVE TO:

EXT. RIVER—THE PBR—DAY

The boat passes rows of skulls, flaming torches, men
impaled on poles, etc.

                 Willard (V.O.)
      Part of me was afraid of what I would find,
      and what I would do when I got there. I
      knew the risks. Or imagined I knew. But the
      thing I felt the most, much stronger than
      fear, was the desire to confront him.

Lance is at the back of the boat, moving in a slow-motion Tai Chi.

DISSOLVE TO:

EXT. RIVER—PBR—DAY

The PBR is slowly moving TOWARD CAMERA. Lance and Willard are standing on the bow of the boat. Chef is at the helm. The men stare forward in amazement. Willard has the binoculars around his neck. He brings them up to his eyes and looks.

> **Willard**
> *(to Chef)*
> Just keep moving.
> *(to Lance)*
> Lance, keep your hands away from the guns.

OUR VIEW MOVES slowly behind them and we SEE what they see.

Hundreds of Montagnard natives, body and faces painted in white, of the most savage nature, but there is a purity about them. Men and boys stand passively on canoes side by side, blocking the river.

There are also hundreds of other NATIVES lining the shore on both sides, dressed in a most ornate and primitive manner, in feathers, parts of birds and animals. Fires and dead bodies are everywhere.

OUR VIEW MOVES

Behind the PBR, closer and closer to this fantastic human wall blocking them. The natives accept the PBR, allowing it to pass into them with a sort of inevitability.

VIEW ON WILLARD, LANCE, AND CHEF

Reacting as they pass through the natives on canoes, then look up toward the banks.

WHAT THEY SEE:

The temple. A magnificent fortified encampment built around the ruins of a former Cambodian civilization.

NEW ANGLE—FULL VIEW BEHIND THE PBR AS IT PROCEEDS

The scale of this thing is enormous. Great enigmatic Cambodian faces carved out of stone from thousands of years ago. The fortress reaches out across the river where part of its ruins still stand on the opposite side and on a small island. It's as though the river flowed into the great arms of the sphinxlike temple. Aligning the fortifications are concertina wire, automatic weapons emplacements. There is even wreckage of Hueys as armed machine gun nests. It is a strange combination of the very modern and the very primitive. In this installation, WE SEE LIVING families, fires, nomadic dwellings, several HUNDRED of the most primitive MONTAGNARDS that ever existed. Some carry spears, occasionally others emerge from the jungle, scurrying around with the activity that

the arrival of a stranger brings. The air is heavy
with the weight of hundreds of AUTOMATIC WEAPONS.
A thick greasy smoke hangs from fires that burn and
around the fort. Fresh shell craters indicate a
recent battle. Near the dock, and everywhere else,
there are tangled piles of corpson, half-submerged
in the water, piles of bodies of the dead.

As the PBR moves up, a HEAD suddenly is thrust into
VIEW. The head is that of a particularly wild,
long-haired, stubble-faced MAN. He has three or
four camera bodies around his neck; a large bag
stuffed with lenses and film. He is dressed in rags
and tatters. He shouts out.

> ### Photographer
> It's all right! It's all right! It's all
> been approved!

The PBR moves slowly toward the steps, as the man
continues to shout out.

> ### Chef
> I ain't coming in there! Them bastards
> attacked us!

> ### Photographer
> Zap 'em with your siren, man. Zap 'em with
> your siren.

Chef BLOWS THE SIREN on the PBR. The Natives react,
never having heard one before; they scatter in all
directions, running away scared.

The photographer moves down onto the landing,
directing the boat.

> ### Photographer
> There's mines over there! Mines over there,

too! And watch out, those goddamn monkeys
bite you, I tell you.

The PBR crew is exhausted, staring at him through
their mud- and blood-spattered faces.

Photographer
Move it in right toward me.

He jumps onboard the boat and immediately advances
toward Lance. He shakes his hand, moves to the others, and shakes their hands as well.

Photographer
I'm an American. An American civilian. Hi,
Yanks. Hi. American. American civilian. It's
all right.
(to Chef)
And you got the cigarettes, and that's what
I've been dreaming of.

Chef flips him a packet of cigarettes.

Willard
(to photographer)
Who are you?

Photographer
Who are you? I'm a photojournalist. I've
covered the war since '64. I've been in
Laos, Cambodia, 'Nam . . .
(looking around the boat)
I'll tell you one thing. This boat is a
mess, man.

Willard
(gestures to matives)
Who are all these people?

Photographer

They think you've come to take him away. I
hope that isn't true.

Willard

Take who away?

Photographer
(gestures to temple)
Him! Colonel Kurtz! These are all his children, man, as far as you can see. Hell, man,
out here, we are all his children.

Willard

Could we talk to Colonel Kurtz?

Photographer

Hey, man, you don't talk to the colonel.
Well, you listen to him.

Willard steps off the boat onto the steps. He turns
and looks back at the photographer.

Photographer

The man's enlarged my mind. He's a poet-
warrior in a classic sense. I mean, sometimes he'll—well, you say hello to him,
right? And he'll just walk right by you and
he won't even notice you. And then suddenly
he'll grab you and he'll throw you in a
corner and he'll say, "Do you know that
'if' is the middle word in 'life'? If you
can keep your head when all about you are
losing theirs and blaming it on you. If you
can trust yourself when all men doubt you."
I'm a little man, I'm a little man. He's a
great man.
(beat)

"I should have been a pair of ragged claws
scuttling across floors of silent seas."

Willard, incredulous, turns away to Lance.

Willard
Stay with the boat.

Photographer
Don't go without me, okay? I want to get a
picture.

Willard and Chef start up the steps. The photographer walks with them, taking photos.

TRACKING SHOT

They reach the top of the steps. Gradually the
natives and savages show themselves—fierce and
frightening, jungle fighters, mostly Montagnard.
They wear only loincloths and bandoleers of
ammunition. Their bodies are painted in strange
patters. Death and parts of bodies are everywhere.

Photographer
He can be terrible, and he can be mean, and
he can be right. He's fighting the war. He's
a great man. I mean, I wish I had words, you
know? I wish I had words. I could tell you
something like, the other day he wanted to
kill me.

Willard
Why did he want to kill you?

They come to a stop.

Photographer
Because I took his picture. He said, "If you
take my picture again, I'm going to kill
you." And he meant it. See, just lay cool,
lay cool. Lay back, dig it.

They start walking forward again, as the photographer continues.

Photographer
He gets friendly again, he really does. But
you don't judge the colonel. You don't judge
the colonel like an ordinary man.

ANGLE ON WILLARD

looking carefully as he moves forward

MOVING POV

More natives and savages. Interspersed among them
are a few taller men with paler skins, with the
remnants of army insignia on them.

ANGLE ON WILLARD

reacting, as he moves forward. Chef is frightened,
as he follows Willard.

ANOTHER ANGLE

They move closer and closer to the temple. The photographer runs up ahead of Willard and stops in

front of the men with paler skins . . . these are remnants of the Green Beret "A" Team.

>   **Photographer**
> Okay, watch it now! These are Americans!
> Americans!
> *(to Willard)*
> You can feel the vibe of this place. Let me
> take a picture. Hey, could you hold it?
> Hello? Could you hold it for a minute?

The photographer starts clicking away with a Nikon, as Willard moves toward what once must have been an American. He wears only shotgun cartridge and striker pants. His face is darkened from dirt, battle smoke, matted with mud and grease.

Willard stops and looks at him.

>   **Willard**
> Colby.

Colby is silent. Then he and the other Berets, women, children, etc., slowly part, making way for Willard. Willard slowly moves through the group and looks.

WHAT HE SEES

The stone steps of the temple. Resting on the steps are freshly severed heads, blood washing down from them. They sit decorating the entrance to the temple like so many gruesome pumpkins.

>   **Photographer**
> The heads. You're looking at the heads.
> Sometimes he goes too far, and he's the first
> one to admit it.

Chef, behind Willard, looks at the heads.

> **Chef**
> He's gone crazy.

> **Photographer**
> Wrong! Wrong! If you could have heard the man just two days ago, if you could've heard him then. God. You were gonna call him crazy?

> **Chef**
> Fucking A.

> **Willard**
> I just want to talk to him.

> **Photographer**
> Well, man, he's gone away. He disappeared out in the jungle with his people.

He continues forward. The others follow.

> **Willard**
> I'll wait for him.

> **Photographer**
> He feels comfortable with his people. He forgets himself with his people. He forgets himself.

> **Chef**
> Captain, maybe we should wait back at the boat.

> **Willard**
> *(turns back to him)*
> Okay, Chef, we'll go back to the boat for a while.

                    Chef
Yeah. Stay with Lance.

EXT. KURTZ COMPOUND—DUSK

MED. SHOT STONE TEMPLE

A STONE HEAD with palm leaves hanging over it.

EXT. PBR—DUSK

Lance is squatting at the bow of the boat holding a
spear, sticking it into the water, probably trying
to spear a fish.

A GROUP OF NATIVES are gathered by the steps of the
dock. One of the natives climbs the tree next to
the dock and cuts loose a dead body. It falls into
the river with a splash.

Chef sits next to Willard in the cabin.

                    Chef
This colonel guy, he's wacko, man. He's
worse than crazy, he's evil! That's what
the man's got set up here, man! It's fucking pagan idolatry! Look around you! Shit,
he's loco.

Willard is putting on his tiger shirt.

                    Willard
Then you'll help me?

                    Chef
Fucking A, I'll help you. I'll do anything

to get out of this joint! We could blow all them assholes away.

CAMERA PANS the savages onshore, who have gathered around them, watching them. We SEE a sign written in a wild hand with white spray paint on a wall: "OUR MOTTO: APOCALYPSE NOW!"

Chef
They're so fucking spaced out, they wouldn't even know it. I ain't afraid of all them fucking skulls and altars and shit. I used to think that if I died in an evil place, then my soul wouldn't be able to make it to heaven. But now . . . fuck. I don't care where it goes, as long as it ain't here. So what do you want to do? I'll kill the fuck.

Willard
(picks up a map)
No, no. I'm gonna need you to wait here, Chef. I'll go up with Lance and scrounge around, check the place out, see if I can find the colonel, okay?

Chef
But what do you want me to do? Damnit.

Willard picks up a field radio and hands it to Chef. Chef looks at it.

Willard
Here, you take the radio, and if I don't get back by 22:00 hours, you call in the air strike.

Chef stares at him.

                              Chef
Air strike?

                           Willard
The code is "Almighty," coordinates zero-
nine-two-six-four-seven-one-two. It's all
in there.

He hands the map to Chef.

EXT. KURTZ COMPOUND—DAY

Willard and Lance walk through the temple grounds
in the rain. Willard is gradually surrounded by
more and more native soldiers.

                        Willard (V.O.)
Everything I saw told me that Kurtz had gone
insane. The place was full of bodies. North
Vietnamese, Vietcong, Cambodians . . . If I
was still alive, it was because he wanted me
that way.

The soldiers close in on him, pick him up, and turn
him upside down, rolling him in the mud.

LOW ANGLE—LANCE

He is slowly walking among passing natives. He is
oblivious to what is happening to Willard.

MED. SHOT WILLARD

Being turned in mud by the natives.

INT. KURTZ QUARTERS—DAY

Willard, hands tied behind his back, is guided down a long corridor, followed by two Montagnards, both armed.

> **Willard (V.O.)**
> It smelled like slow death in there. Malaria and nightmares. This was the end of the river, all right.

They turn into the main room. The natives indicate for Willard to kneel down on the floor. The CAMERA MOVES, REVEALING KURTZ lying in shadow on a bed. We will SEE him only in darkness and shadow throughout the scene.

> **Kurtz**
> Where you from, Willard?

> **Willard**
> I'm from Ohio, sir.

> **Kurtz**
> Were you born there?

> **Willard**
> Yes, sir.

> **Kurtz**
> Whereabouts?

> **Willard**
> Toledo, sir.

Kurtz

How far are you from the river?

Willard

The Ohio River, sir? About two hundred miles.

Kurtz

I went down that river once when I was a kid. There's a place in the river, I can't remember . . . must have been a gardenia plantation, or a flower plantation at one time. It's all wild and overgrown now. But for about five miles, you'd think that heaven just fell on the earth, in the form of gardenias.

Kurtz reaches down and picks up a bowl full of water. He splashes water on his face and head.

Kurtz

Have you ever considered, any real freedoms? Freedoms from the opinions of others. Even the opinions of yourself. Did they say why, Willard? Why they wanted to terminate my command?

Willard

I was sent on a classified mission, sir.

Kurtz

It's no longer classified, is it. What did they tell you?

Willard

They told me, that you had gone . . . totally insane. And that your methods were unsound.

                    Kurtz
Are my methods unsound?

                    Willard
I don't see any method at all, sir.

                    Kurtz
I expected someone like you. What did you
expect? Are you an assassin?

                    Willard
I'm a soldier.

We finally SEE KURTZ'S FACE.

                    Kurtz
You're neither. You're an errand boy, sent
by grocery clerks, to collect a bill.

EXT. KURTZ COMPOUND—TRAIL UP FROM RIVER—DAY

The photographer hurries down the trail past villagers and soldiers toward the compound, and up the
hill that leads toward the TIGER CAGES in front of
the Monkey Temple. He spots a jug full of water,
with a ladle in it.

AT TIGER CAGES—TO GO WITH PHOTOGRAPHER

The photographer moves to Willard who is in a
tiger cage. Willard is in pretty bad shape, weak
and thirsty. The photographer stops in front of
him. He holds the ladle for Willard to drink
from.

Photographer

Why? Why would a nice guy like you want to kill a genius? Feeling pretty good, huh? Why? Do you know that the man really likes you?

He puts a cigarette in Willard's mouth.

Photographer

He likes you. He really likes you. But he's got something in mind for you. Aren't you curious about that? I'm curious. I'm very curious. Are you curious?

The photographer walks around Willard's cage.

Photographer

There's something happening out here, man. You know something, man? I know something that you don't know. That's right, Jack. The man is clear in his mind, but his soul is mad. Oh, yeah. He's dying, I think. He hates all this. He hates it! But the man's a . . . He reads poetry out loud, all right? And a voice . . . he likes you 'cause you're still alive. He's got plans for you. No, I'm not gonna help you. You're gonna help him, man. You're gonna help him. I mean, what are they gonna say when he's gone? 'Cause he dies when it dies, when it dies, he dies! What are they gonna say about him? He was a kind man? He was a wise man? He had plans? He had wisdom? Bullshit, man! Am I gonna be the one that's gonna set them straight? Look at me! Wrong!
  (points at Willard)
You.

EXT. PBR—RAIN—DAY

Chef is sleeping ondeck in the rain, under a tarp.

Chef

    (to himself)
Almost eight hours. I'm asleep. I'm asleep
and dreaming I'm on this shitty boat. Fuck.
Has it been eight hours?

He lifts the tarp off, gets up, and goes to the
cabin.

HIGH **ANGLE** ON PBR

It is raining.

Chef (O.S.)

    (into radio)
Hello. Almighty. Almighty. This is PBR Street
Gang. Radio check, over.

Male Voice (Over Radio)

PBR Street Gang, this is Almighty standing
by, over.

EXT. KURTZ COMPOUND—NIGHT

CLOSE ON KURTZ'S BOOTS

Walking on wet ground.

ANGLE ON **WILLARD** IN **TIGER** CAGE

covered with mud, tied up and wet from rain. He slowly looks up.

KURTZ IS STANDING OVER HIM. He is dressed in the black pajamas of the Vietcong. His face is made up in green-and-black camouflage paint. He disappears behind Willard, then reappears and drops something into Willard's lap. Willard looks down and sees CHEF'S SEVERED HEAD in his lap.

Willard screams and struggles to jostle it out of his lap. It finally falls out.

CLOSE ON CHEF'S HEAD

in the mud.

CLOSE ON WILLARD

moaning.

> Willard
>
> Oh, Christ!

DISSOLVE TO:

INT. CONEX CONTAINER—DAY

Willard is passed out, lying on the floor of a metal CONEX CONTAINER. It is hot. Some CHILDREN are peeking in at him.

The two front doors of the container are opened. Light floods in. Kurtz is standing there with the children. He holds a bunch of magazine articles.

He sits down on a dirt step, surrounded by children.

He looks down at a magazine article and begins to read it to Willard.

> **Kurtz**
> *(reading)*
> "*Time* magazine. The weekly news magazine. September 22, 1967, volume ninety, number twelve. The War on the Horizon. The American people may find it hard to believe that the U.S. is winning the war in Vietnam. Nevertheless, one of the most exhaustive inquiries into the status of the conflict yet compiled, offers considerable evidence that the weight of U.S. power, two and a half years after the big buildup began, is beginning to make itself felt. "White House officials maintain the impact of that strength may bring the enemy to the point where he could simply be unable to continue fighting."
> *(to Willard)*
> Is this familiar?

Willard reacts.

> **Kurtz**
> *(reading)*
> "Because Lyndon Johnson fears that the U.S. public is in no mood to accept its optimistic conclusions, he may never permit the report to be released in full. Even so, he is sufficiently impressed with the findings, and sufficiently anxious to make their conclusions known, to permit experts who have been working on it to talk about it in general terms." No date,

Time magazine. "Sir Robert Thompson, who led the victory over Communist guerrillas in Malay, and is now a RAND Corporation consultant, recently returned to Vietnam to sound out the situation for President Nixon. He told the president last week that things felt much better, and smelled much better over there."

He looks over at Willard.

>   **Kurtz**
>   *(to Willard)*
>   How do they smell to you, soldier?

Willard doesn't answer. Kurtz rises. The children are laughing and giggling. Kurtz drops the magazine articles in Willard's lap.

>   **Kurtz**
>   You'll be free. You'll be under guard. Read
>   these at your leisure. Don't lose them.
>   Don't try to escape, you'll be shot. We can
>   talk of these things later.

Kurtz turns and exits, closing one of the doors, leaving the other open. Willard watches him go. The children stay, looking at him, laughing and giggling. Willard slowly and painfully pulls himself to his feet. He stands there a moment looking at the children, then collapses to the floor.

>   DISSOLVE TO:

EXT. KURTZ COMPOUND—HIGH **ANGLE—DAY**

The river and temple.

INT. KURTZ COMPOUND—DAY

An unconscious Willard is being carried by some native soldiers. They lay him gently on the floor of the temple. Ladle water into his mouth, try to feed him rice. He turns his head.

WHAT HE SEES

Kurtz, in the shadows.

DISSOLVE TO:

WILLARD, HIS DELIRIUM

NATIVE EATING BOWL OF RICE IN CORRIDOR

DISSOLVE TO:

KURTZ CATCHING A FLY

DISSOLVE TO:

STONE STATUES

> Kurtz (O.S.)
> (reading)
> "We are the hollow men are the stuffed men together filled with straw. Alas dried voices, when whisper together quiet and

meaningless wind in dried grass rats' feet
over broken glass our dry cellar."

DISSOLVE TO:

WILLARD AND THE PHOTOGRAPHER

in Kurtz's chamber. Willard is lying on a bed of
sandbags. The photographer is next to him. They are
both listening to Kurtz read the poem.

>   **Photographer**
> He's really out there.

ANGLE ON KURTZ

seated on a small chest next to his bed. He is
reading from a small book. It is "The Hollow Man"
by T. S. Eliot.

>   **Kurtz**
>   *(reading)*
>   "Shape without form, shade without color,
>   force, gesture without motion;"

>   **Photographer**
> Do you know what the man's saying? Do you?

>   **Kurtz**
>   *(reading)*
>   "Those who have crossed direct eyes . . ."

>   **Photographer**
> This is dialectics. It's very simple dialec-
> tics. It's one through nine, no maybes, no
> supposes, no fractions. You can't travel in
> space. You can't go out into space, without

like, you know, with fractions. What are you
gonna land on? One quarter? Three-eighths?
What are you gonna do when you go from here
to Venus? That's dialectic physics, okay?
Dialectic logic is, there's only love and
hate. You either love somebody, or you hate
them.

Kurtz throws a bunch of bananas at the photographer.

Kurtz
Mutt! You mutt.

Photographer
This is the way the fucking world lives.
Look at this fucking shit we're in, man! Not
with a bang. Whimper. And with a whimper,
I'm fucking splitting, Jack.

Photographer rises and exits down the corridor,
leaving Willard alone. Kurtz looks at him.

DISSOLVE TO:

INT. KURTZ'S QUARTERS—DAY

Willard is at a table containing Kurtz's belong-
ings. He looks at his uniform, military decorations, photographs of Kurtz' family, a Bible, and
other books lying on the table.

Willard (V.O.)
On the river, I thought that the minute I
looked at him, I'd know what to do. But it
didn't happen. I was in there with him for
days. Not under guard. I was free. But he
knew I wasn't going anywhere. He knew more

about what I was going to do than I did. If
the generals back in Nha Trang could see
what I saw, would they still want me to kill
him? More than ever, probably. And what
would his people back home want, if they
ever learned just how far from them he'd
really gone. He broke from them, and then he
broke from himself. I'd never seen a man so
broken up and ripped apart.

ANGLE ON DOORWAY

Kurtz enters in the darkness.

> **Kurtz**
> I've seen horrors. Horrors that you've seen.
> But you have no right to call me a murderer.
> You have a right to kill me. You have a right
> to do that. But you have no right to judge
> me.

CLOSE UP ON KURTZ

eating a piece of fruit.

> **Kurtz**
> It's impossible for words to describe what
> is necessary to those who do not know what
> horror means. Horror. Horror has a face. And
> you must make a friend of horror. Horror and
> moral terror are your friends. If they are
> not, then they are enemies to be feared.
> They are truly enemies.

ANOTHER ANGLE

Colby is standing in the rear doorway of the main temple, going through a Tai Chi routine. Willard sits in front of him, looking at Kurtz, listening to him as he talks from the bed. A native WOMAN is there, listening as well.

Kurtz

I remember when I was with Special Forces. Seems a thousand centuries ago. We went into a camp to inoculate some children. We'd left the camp after we had inoculated the children for polio. And this old man came running after us, and he was crying. He couldn't say. We went back there, and they had come and hacked off every inoculated arm. There they were, in a pile. A pile of little arms. And, I remember, I cried, I wept like some grandmother. I wanted to tear my teeth out. I didn't know what I wanted to do. And I want to remember it. I never want to forget it. I never want to forget. And then I realized, like I was shot, like I was shot with a diamond, a diamond bullet right through my forehead. And I thought, My God, the genius of that! The genius. The will to do that. Perfect, genuine, complete, crystalline, pure. And then I realized, they were stronger than we. Because they could stand it. These were not monsters. These were men, trained cadres. These men who fought with their hearts, who have families, who have children, who are filled with love . . . that they had the strength, the strength to do that. If I had ten divisions of those men, then our troubles here would be over very quickly. You have to have men who are moral, and at the same time, who are able to utilize their primordial instincts to

kill without feeling, without passion.
Without judgment. Without judgment. Because
it's judgment that defeats us.

CLOSE ON WILLARD

He slowly raises his hand, and examines it.

Kurtz
I worry that my son might not understand
what I've tried to be. And if I were to be
killed, Willard, I would want someone to
go to my home and tell my son everything . . .

DISSOLVE TO:

ANGLE ON KURTZ

standing in the doorway of the temple. We SEE a
WATER BUFFALO in the foreground, walking down the
steps.

EXT. TEMPLE—CEREMONIAL GROUNDS—NIGHT

NATIVES are conducting a ceremony. They are dancing
and singing around the WATER BUFFALO. A priest is
chanting.

Kurtz (V.O.)
Everything I did. Everything you saw.
Because there's nothing that I detest more
than the stench of lies. And if you understand me, Willard, you will do this for me.

Lance is sitting with the natives, painted and dressed like one of them. A line of natives with spears dance toward the water buffalo. Others are sitting and singing in the background.

EXT.—THE PBR—NIGHT

It has been deserted except for monkeys crawling on it.

> **Male Voice (Over Radio)**
> PBR Street Gang, this is Almighty standing by, over. PBR Street Gang, this is Almighty standing by. How do you copy?

CLOSE ON WILLARD

On the boat, lying on his back. He rolls over.

> **Willard (V.O.)**
> They were gonna make me a major for this, and I wasn't even in their fucking army anymore. Everybody wanted me to do it. Him most of all. I felt like he was up there, waiting for me to take the pain away. He just wanted to go out like a soldier.

He gets up and emerges out of the darkness.

> **Willard (V.O.)**
> Standing up. Not like some poor, wasted rag-assed renegade. Even the jungle wanted him dead. And that's who he really took his orders from, anyway.

EXT. TEMPLE—NIGHT

ANGLE ON LANCE

smearing the water buffalo with blood that he pours from a pitcher along its neck, in preparation for the ceremony.

MIST OVER WATER

A small bubble rises to the surface, then another. Suddenly but quietly, water and mud pour off revealing Willard, emerging slowly, head first, as if he was growing out of the water.

WATER BUFFALO

Its head being tied to a stake.

KURTZ

Silhouetted in the doorway of the temple. He enters the temple.

WILLARD

sits crouched holding a machete as natives dance in the background He rises slowly and then runs off.

INSIDE THE TEMPLE

Willard works his way toward the interior of the temple. He appears behind a guard, puts his hand over the warrior's mouth, brings up the machete, and pulls him back into the dark shadows.

INTERCUT THE FOLLOWING ACTION WITH WATER BUFFALO CEREMONY:

Kurtz is sitting and talking into a tape recorder. Willard slowly moves forward, quietly sneaking toward Kurtz as he speaks.

>   Kurtz (Into Recorder)
> We train young men to drop fire on people,
> but their commanders won't allow them to
> write "fuck" on their airplanes because it's
> obscene.

Willard steps behind Kurtz, raising the machete. Kurtz turns. Willard brings the knife down and starts hacking away at Kurtz, hitting him first on the shoulder, then all over.

NATIVES

simultaneously slashing a knife into the back of the water buffalo.

KURTZ

falls to the floor.

WATER BUFFALO

falling to the ground as natives swing knives into
its back.

WILLARD

staring at Kurtz.

CLOSE ON KURTZ

lying on the ground.

                         Kurtz
    The horror . . . the horror.

He dies.

CLOSE ON WILLARD

hands on his face, reacting to what he's done

                                      DISSOLVE TO:

NATIVES AND LANCE

around dead water buffalo, carving it up.

                                      DISSOLVE TO:

WILLARD

stands at the temple entrance. He looks at the
natives outside. He walks over to Kurtz's desk.
Flips through Kurtz's manuscript and stops. We SEE

handwriting on the page: "Drop the Bomb, Exterminate them all."

EXT. FRONT OF TEMPLE—NIGHT

The natives are all gathered in front of the temple, looking at Willard as he moves forward holding the machete and Kurtz's books. The entire village is there, about a THOUSAND NATIVES in all. They realize that Willard is now their leader and pay HOMAGE to him by kneeling or sitting down.

Willard slowly walks down the steps, throwing down the machete. The natives rise and throw down their weapons in imitation as he walks through them. He moves to LANCE, who is in the midst of all the natives. Willard looks at him, then takes him by the hand and pulls him away with him through the rest of the natives.

DISSOLVE TO:

EXT. PBR—RAIN—NIGHT

The PBR pulls away from the shore. Willard is at the helm of the boat. Lance is squatting by the spotlight.

> **Male Voice (Over Radio)**
> Calling PBR Street Gang. PBR Street Gang, this is Almighty. Do you read me? Over. PBR Street Gang, this is Almighty.

Willard turns off the radio.

The PBR moves along the river, away from the flaming shoreline.

CLOSE ON WILLARD

                    Kurtz (V.O.)
          The horror . . . the horror.

                                        DISSOLVE TO:

THE GREAT STONE FACE OF THE TEMPLE

                                        FADE OUT

MARLON BRANDO
ROBERT DUVALL
MARTIN SHEEN

in

"APOCALYPSE NOW REDUX"

FREDERIC FORREST
ALBERT HALL
SAM BOTTOMS
LAURENCE FISHBURNE
CHRISTIAN MARQUAND
AURORE CLEMENT
HARRISON FORD
and DENNIS HOPPER

produced and directed by
FRANCIS FORD COPPOLA

written by
JOHN MILIUS and FRANCIS FORD COPPOLA

narration by
MICHAEL HERR

co-produced by FRED ROOS,
GRAY FREDERICKSON and TOM STERNBERG

cinematographer
VITTORIO STORARO
a.i.c.-a.s.c.

production designer
DEAN TAVOULARIS

editor
RICHARD MARKS

sound design by
WALTER MURCH

music by
CARMINE COPPOLA and FRANCIS FORD COPPOLA

"APOCALYPSE NOW REDUX"
version produced by
FRANCIS FORD COPPOLA and KIM AUBRY

editor
WALTER MURCH

A MIRAMAX FILMS RELEASE
AN AMERICAN ZOETROPE PRODUCTION